Tales of the Crusades

Tales of the Crusades

OLIVIA COOLIDGE

1970

HOUGHTON MIFFLIN COMPANY BOSTON

Also by OLIVIA COOLIDGE

Greek Myths
Legends of the North
The Trojan War
Egyptian Adventures
Cromwell's Head
Roman People
Winston Churchill
    and the Story of Two World Wars
Caesar's Gallic War
Men of Athens
Makers of the Red Revolution
People in Palestine
Lives of Famous Romans
The King of Men
Marathon Looks on the Sea
George Bernard Shaw
The Maid of Artemis

Contents

Introduction

It is impossible to give in a few short stories a complete picture of a movement which lasted almost four hundred years and involved three civilizations — medieval Christian, Greek Christian, and Moslem. Any fictional writer who chooses the Crusades has to select.

What, then, shall we bring out? It is tempting to suggest that the achievements of the Crusades are what we ought to dwell on. Historians hasten to assure us that there are none. The creation of a kingdom in the East was temporary and left no permanent mark. The contact between East and West which resulted from the kingdom, or even from the clash of war, was less fruitful than the contact of the two cultures in Sicily or Spain, where they lived side by side for centuries. Trade flourished in spite of, rather than because of, the Crusades.

Two negative results to which historians have seemed to give more weight are the destruction of the power of the Greek Empire and a general disillusion with the Papacy and the Church.

Yet when we look at even these, they dissolve under scrutiny. The Greek Empire was so beset at the beginning of the crusading period by Moslems in the East and by Christians in the West that it is hard to imagine its lasting longer if the Crusades had never taken place. The sack of Constantinople by the Fourth Crusade was indeed a tragedy, but it cannot bear all the blame for a decay that had already set in. Similarly it is true that the Popes found it convenient to have an army under control of the Church. This soon tempted them to use crusades against German Emperors or other princes at a time when there was no clear demarcation between political and spiritual claims. This brought the Papacy and the Crusades themselves into disrepute. Furthermore, it tempted Popes to release crusaders from their vows for money in order to hire more efficient troops. By no means every pilgrim was a fighter. Nevertheless, the conditions which corrupted Pope Urban's ideal would still have existed had the Crusades never taken place. Temporal and spiritual powers were bound to come into conflict, forcing the Church to act in ways which were no better than those of her opponents.

Must we, then, dismiss the Crusades as a mistaken movement which failed to leave any mark upon its times, unless it were possibly to make the faith of Islam more militant and less tolerant than before? This judgment seems unfair to the enormous effort which the West, and especially France, put forth for centuries.

What we ought to do is to forget what might have happened and look more closely at what did. Through the Crusades, the West did in fact contact the East, destroy Constantinople, become disillusioned with Papal power and with the Church. It is through the crusading adventure that these things actually happened, even if without it they might have occurred some other way. Into the Crusades people poured their faith, their energy, their greed, their folly. The Crusades are not history because they did what they meant to do or unintentionally did other things, but because the medieval world worked out its problems through them.

This allows us to look at the Crusades from a realistic point of view. What did people mean by them, and how did this meaning change as centuries wore by? What qualities of faith and courage, what faults of selfishness did men invest in them? It is not enough to look back from our present age and dismiss them, saying their cause was not worthwhile or their results were negative. History is the story of what went on, not of what we think about it. The Crusades embodied the medieval spirit, changing as that spirit changed and fading as it faded. Thus they formed part of a pattern which cannot be seen without them. History is different later on because the medieval situation was developed through the Crusades, and not through some other ideal.

Tales of the Crusades

PROLOGUE

The Emperor

1094

Wɪɴᴅ ʙʟᴇᴡ in Constantinople, surging up from the West with clouds streaming like the squadrons of an invading army. It swirled around the towers of the triple wall, leaped over them, and raced along the ridge, whistling down the arcades of fabulous shops and causing citizens to pull their fur-trimmed hats about their ears. The Emperor of the Romans, riding in procession through the streets to visit the church of the Mother of God, was buffeted by this wind like a common man. It tore at his garments of silk brocade and even tried to tumble off his headdress, weighed down though it was with precious stones and pearls big as a pigeon's egg. Alexius Comnenus rode through this assault like a soldier, merely blinking as the cold brought tears to his eyes. Riding on a white ass the Patriarch, God's bishop, clutched at his garments, which the wind was trying to blow above his knees.

Alexius was received at Blachernae by the monks who served God's Mother; while the wind, having scattered a few tiles and dropped hats in the gutter, roared away across the straits to Asia Minor. It disappeared down the great road built long ago by Persian kings and kept up for a thousand years by Emperors of the Romans. It was a road now lost to the Roman power, together with the lands to which it led: Asia Minor, made famous by St. Paul; the birthplace of Our Lord; His holy Sepulchre; and other once-Christian lands still more remote. These parts were Moslem territory now, through which the wind drove its cloud-army, leaving Constantinople, once capital of half the world, to an ominous quiet.

It was not until noon when he had returned from Blachernae that Alexius gave audience in his octagonal throne-room, which was floored in porphyry and precious marbles, bright with mosaics, and glittering with vast golden chandeliers. The flames of countless candles glowed on the golden walls and flickered over the lions and griffins of gold that guarded the throne in its arched alcove. Alexius sat perfectly still with his hands on his knees, so swathed in silk brocade flashing with golden threads, so covered in jewels that he might have been merely a part of the throne, were it not for his dark eyes and the jutting beak of his nose and his short, black beard.

His chamberlains brought the barbarians in, some twenty of them, all youngish men much travel-stained, with uncut flowing hair and yellow moustaches. They knelt, as they had been instructed to do, in the red circle on the floor and bowed their heads. As though at a signal, the golden lions raised their tails and started to roar; the griffins hissed, clattering their scales.

The barbarians sprang to their feet in dismay. Their young leader, who wore an armlet of gold, felt at his belt for a weapon that was not there. But seeing that the beasts did not advance, he glanced quickly at the barbarian axeman standing beside the throne as though he sought instruction.

The guard's eyes caught those of the young man and slid away to fix themselves on the second circle in the floor, the green one, on which the second act of homage was to be performed. Reassured, the young barbarian took a few steps forward and sank to his knees again. After a little pause, the others followed. Instantly a silence fell, and the golden monsters resumed the stiff poses of metal. The barbarians bowed again; and as they did so, the birds in a golden tree to the right of the throne began to move and twitter.

The young man stared at the tree as he got to his feet. Nothing he had heard of the mightiest city on earth had prepared him for the knowledge that the secrets of Paradise were known here, so that lifeless things could move and

speak. In the third circle, the circle of gold, his knees sagged
under him almost willingly, and he bowed his head to the
very floor.

The birds fell silent, but he heard a rumble. Cautiously
he looked up, and his mouth fell open in a foolish expression. In front of him were the seven steps to the throne. Beside it stood the guard, axe on shoulder. On either side were
ranged the officials of the court in glittering garments. The
golden throne and the emperor had vanished.

The axeman cast his eyes up; and the young man discovered the emperor near the ceiling, apparently suspended
on air. Here Alexius sat, motionless as before, his gaze fixed
on the Mother of God depicted on the opposite wall.

The young man stared. He had been carefully primed
with what he was to say, but he felt the awkwardness of
craning his neck to speak to one so far above him. Silence
followed in which nobody moved. The courtiers stood waiting, while the golden beasts and birds sat perfectly still. Presently the young man swallowed and cleared his throat. "I,
Sweyn, son of Edgar, son of Morcar, who was Earl of North-
umberland before the Conqueror's time, have come with
these my housecarls to enter service in your Varangian
Guard."

He spoke in Saxon, and behind him the chamberlain
translated into Greek. Without deigning to look down, the
Emperor gave a slow nod. A white silk curtain slid across
the alcove, blotting him from sight. Sweyn and his followers backed clumsily across the hall of audience, bowing as
they went.

Such was the dignity of the Emperor in his hall of audience. In his private apartments, though these were equally rich, his effect was not the same. Alexius was a little man, short-legged and broad of shoulder. His face, now that he permitted it to show expression, looked tired. There were pouches under his eyes and wrinkles in his forehead, though his hair and beard were not yet gray. He sat on a chair with a back, while his intimate councilors, his brother Isaac, the Patriarch, and the Grand Domestic of the Palace, sat on stools.

Alexius glowed in garments nearly as splendid as those he had worn in his hall of audience; but the robes of his courtiers, which had glittered handsomely in the light of the golden chandeliers, might now be seen to be dirty at hem and rubbed at elbow. These were ceremonial clothes kept in the Palace and donned only when they visited it. The Grand Domestic still wore his father's, which were too small. Isaac Comnenus had shrunken a little with age, and his were too large.

"This is the greatest city of the world," Alexius complained, "a city of a million people. Yet I, the Emperor of the Romans, receive the grandson of a petty Saxon chief for no better reason than that he brings me twenty men to join my guard."

The comment was not addressed to anyone, so that only Isaac, who was greatly privileged, could venture to answer. "It is nearly thirty years," he said, prefacing his statement with a formal inclination of his head towards his brother, "since William the Norman conquered England. We have many Saxons in our guard, but they grow old. These young men born in exile will be the last recruits from Saxon England. None of the Norsemen have taken service here for years. Gold will not buy them any more."

"I have played our enemies against each other," Alexius sighed, "and won us respite where I can. We have to defend ourselves or be conquered. Tribes press down from the North. To the West there are the Bulgars. The Normans have taken Italy from us and invaded Greece. Meanwhile, in Asia Minor, the Turk stands at our very gates. I must have men!"

He looked at the Patriarch, who fumbled for a moment at his beard, quite evidently surprised at being consulted on a military matter. He bowed his head to the Emperor, however, and answered as befitted his position. "We are the city of the Mother of God, whose grace protects us. We have the True Cross in our midst and the bones of Saints beyond counting. Surely our Lord will fight for His own!"

"Even the Lord's army," said Isaac, receiving permission from his brother's glance to speak, "fights with human hands. The graces of Our Lady do not soften infidel hearts." He paused and added grimly, "We have lost our recruiting grounds in Asia Minor."

This seemed so obvious to the Great Domestic, who was also a fighting man, that he sighed heavily. Alexius, however, though he was a greater general than either, disagreed. "Our Lady and the True Cross shall find us men, and the saints shall give them strength. I think to ask the Pope of Rome for volunteers."

"He is no true bishop of Rome," said the Patriarch quickly, "but a heretic in schism."

Alexius shrugged. "That breach may be repaired. What does it amount to except that Latin is a clumsy language, so that a Roman bishop stumbled in defining the mysteries of God? It is in my mind this Urban, who has been driven out of Rome by quarreling factions and who is not even acknowledged as Pope by what the Germans call the Roman Empire, will be glad enough to get rid of some turbulent nobles. Already he directs them to fight the infidel in Spain, calling it a holy war."

"There is no such thing as a holy war," cried the Patriarch, shocked.

"Indeed there is not. Yet may it not be better in the eyes of God to defend Christendom from infidel hosts than to murder Christian neighbors? The feuds of these barbaric peoples are endless, and their men are bred to war. Besides, it must be important for Pope Urban to be reconciled to the True Church."

The Patriarch, more skilled in controversy, looked doubtful; but Alexius would not let him object. "I shall send one of my embassies," he said. "Since this is a matter for very delicate handling, I shall instruct it in person."

Isaac sighed. The embassies of Alexius were famous for the adroitness with which they gained his objects, but envoys were too slow when danger pressed. "What forces can we assemble for the spring campaign?" asked he.

The Pope

1095

Aᴅʜᴇᴍᴀʀ, bishop of Puy, was one of the fortunate persons who had been given a room in the monastery of Clermont. Enormous though the place was, it could not accommodate two hundred and fifty of the senior churchmen of France and all their attendants. Many an abbot had found himself housed with some wealthy merchant or even with a rather humble tradesman. So full to bursting was the town that junior clerics were lucky to get a bed at all, while secular nobles, riding in from distant castles to gape at Pope Urban, were forced to camp in tents, though it was November.

Urban had deliberately housed Adhemar near him because he nursed a great plan for which he needed a lieuten-
ant. None was more loyal than Adhemar, none more tact-
ful, more apt for a lofty scheme, more wise and prudent.
The two men were old friends and now had this secret in
common, so that hardly a day had passed of the great council without a private interview between them.

If the truth had really been known, these talks had settled little, since Urban had thought of all before meeting
Adhemar. Indeed, the bishop's task seemed merely to en-
courage his friend, on whom the burden of statesmanship
lay heavy. "Who could have imagined," Adhemar said on
the last evening, "only a few years back that these French
bishops would dare to join you in excommunicating their
own king!"

"He is a godless man," said Urban, brooding darkly over
his quarrel with King Philip. "His adultery is flagrant." He
shuffled his feet in the rushes covering the cold stone of the
floor and reflected bitterly how he had despised fleshly com-
forts when he was a monk. Now he felt the cold, and they
brought him a cup of hot wine before he went to bed. He
sipped it, torn between pleasure and resentment.

Adhemar set aside his own cup and bent forward to snuff
a candle which was flaring. He was a round-faced little man
of gentle manners, slow speech, and commonplace appearance. Perhaps to make up for this last, he lived in worldly
style, content to bear himself as a great lord rather than a
churchman. Looking at the pair, one would never have

thought that it was Adhemar who had thrown up everything in a spirit of romantic devotion to make a pilgrimage
to Jerusalem from which he was lucky to have returned
alive. Meanwhile Pope Urban, pupil of Saint Bruno and
handsome as a saint himself, struggled with kings in a crude
age, using political methods to advance the cause of God
and the power of His Church.

They smiled at each other with great affection, each perceiving in his friend a quality which he would have liked to
possess. "God is still at work in the world," said Adhemar
gently. "We shall see it tomorrow!"

The Pope leaned his splendid head against the back of his
chair in a weary gesture. "All Christendom sins," he said
sternly, "and none are found righteous. They would be well
served if the Lord were to harden their hearts."

This remark, as Adhemar intuitively perceived, was inspired by stage fright. The Pope had nursed his grand design so long, had so carefully prepared it, so deliberately
sounded out leaders, so dramatically announced a great
speech that his imagination now told him it would fall flat.
Quietly Adhemar resisted the temptation to proffer the
help of Saint Mary of Puy and the Saints.

"It is a good thing," he remarked prosaically, "that you
have a bull-like voice and are a Frenchman. I can make
myself understood in the cathedral, but I could not speak to
so vast a crowd in the open air. All the countryside has been
moving in: lords, pedlars, holy men in rags, poor peasants
who have never been five miles from home before this day.

Because of the truce of God, even notorious brigands have come to pray, hearing a rumor that the Pope will grant forgiveness for their sins."

"Why, so I will," agreed Urban eagerly. "The Lord has work for all who will turn from their evil ways. But tell me, Adhemar, will the great lords come in? Never mind about the peasants!"

"You have the word of Raymond, Count of Toulouse. Where he leads, many will follow."

Urban nodded, agreeing. "Praise God and all His Saints. I shall tell the crowd our great design tomorrow."

"God wills it!" Adhemar exclaimed, his dark eyes sparkling in his undistinguished face. The Pope caught his glance and nodded.

"Truly, God wills it."

The Preacher

LITTLE PETER was a man who saw visions. Our Lady, for instance, appeared to him exactly as she had been painted in a picture of Judgment Day in the church of his boyhood, where he had served mass for the dirty old priest and acted as his servant. In a dream she had come to him there and said, "Get up, Peter, and follow me." He had risen up straight away and had gone out of the hut of the priest, where he slept with the pigs. All sore from a beating as he was, he had followed Mary. Our Lady had led him by devious ways and had protected him from being returned as

a runaway serf. Eventually he had built himself a hut by
Saint-Gobin, not far from Soissons, and had set himself up
as a hermit, begging bread on the highway. Here Mary
had spoken to him again, not once, but very often. She generally spoke in the mind, interrupting the train of his own
thought to tell him, for instance, that her portrait in the
Saint-Gobin church was not like her.

He was often seen in the villages nearby because, though
he knew his Pater and Ave and scraps of the Latin mass,
these were not sufficient to inspire perpetual devotions.
Since he never washed and was content with a rough tunic
and an old cloak much too large, binding rags around his
feet in wintertime, the local peasants thought of him as
one of themselves, except more holy. They asked advice;
and Peter gave it, drawing sometimes on his native shrewd-
ness, but at other times on the inner commands of Our Lady,
which appeared in his mind with their usual suddenness.

In this way, Our Lady told him to lay a curse on the villain
who had robbed and murdered an old pedlar on the highway. Her inspiration gave Peter such eloquence in describ-
ing the pangs of Hell, which he had seen pictured in church,
that a couple of women had hysterics straightaway, while
several people confessed to sins none knew they had committed. It is true that the murderer kept silent, but Our
Lady soon punished him herself. In less than three months
a pestilence swept through the village and carried off several.
Among these was the murderer, who acknowledged his
guilt and died raving.

This example had given great reputation to Peter, who

was by this time preaching in marketplaces or at the gates of towns in a twenty-mile radius. The gift of eloquence which Our Lady had called forth was a genuine one, and Peter's visions were increasing in scope. There were many churches within his circuit, all of them brightly painted. His inner eye would pick out a saint or a devil and tell him that this one was a genuine likeness. In such a way, Peter's world became filled with gold and glory, with fire and brimstone and the monsters of Hell.

Many legends were soon current about Peter. The miracles he performed were not few, and besides his impulses gave rise to talk. He was preaching, for instance, at the gate of Soissons when he saw a poor man coming out on a donkey. Breaking off what he was saying, Peter walked across and took it by the bridle, helping its owner to dismount. Then he put his own leg across its back, thanked Our Lady for the gift, and rode off blessing the giver, who gaped dumbfounded at the preacher's assurance.

After this Peter ranged far and wide, while his donkey became almost as famous as the man. Indeed, Peter was presently moved to acquire a group of disciples, one of whose duties was to protect the unfortunate beast because it was widely believed that a hair from his tail would be potent against the ills of the flesh and possibly, though of this one was less sure, admit one to Heaven.

Pope Urban had looked around on his world and found it bad. Little Peter did the same. No matter how many he moved to repent, the power of the Devil remained as great as ever. Sin was gross and crude and cruel everywhere, while the world was full of sickening things. With her usual abruptness, Our Lady forbade him to preach of Hell and told him to fix men's eyes on the golden towers of Heaven. When Peter obeyed her, his audience fell away. Men had to be frightened into doing good because they understood Hell, but not Heaven.

Peter wandered alone once more, uncertain of his path. He was actually in the center of France when abbots and bishops began to set out for the great Council of Clermont. Their trains passed Peter on the road, and their people told him that the Pope himself was going to give them an answer to the evil in the world. Drawn by this magnet, Peter followed.

Amid the curious crowds which were flocking to Clermont, Little Peter's unwashed smell and long face like his donkey's made no impression. There were holy men of every sort in the throng: faith healers, visionaries, preachers, many with a crowd of followers around them. Little Peter arrived without noise, camping in a corner of the common land with his donkey beside him while he watched the platform set up in the field for the speech of Pope Urban. He gaped at the procession of the princes of the Church, colorful as any painting, winding out of the east gate escorting the Pope.

Urban the Second looked like Saint Peter, whose portrait his little namesake had seen in many churches. The Pope's voice echoed to the farthest corner of the field like the sound of a trumpet. There was a city, a city of the Romans, Pope

Urban called it, which must be Jerusalem itself. It was surrounded by a triple wall of gold, and there were bones of saints within it, together with the True Cross and churches beyond counting. The infidel was at its gates. Peter knew this already because pilgrims did go from time to time to the country where Our Lord was crucified and where Our Lady bore Him. A few returned from the very jaws of death and brought back stories. Never until Pope Urban spoke had these tales and Peter's visions made one whole.

They must go to Jerusalem, Pope Urban said, to win back that country, where the heathen were now killing Christians, burning churches, and desecrating the relics of God Himself. Let brigands become soldiers of Christ. Let mercenaries who had fought for gold now fight for salvation. Let all who had attacked their fellow Christians now smite the enemies of God.

"Put your affairs in order!" Pope Urban cried. "Pledge yourselves without delay, and go home to collect what is needful. As soldiers of Christ your sins shall be forgiven; and those who die in the fight will go straight to Heaven. For those who live, there will be earthly rewards as well as heavenly ones, since the lands of the infidel are rich in plunder. Meanwhile, I take your goods at home under my protection, that none may do you wrong while you are absent."

"God wills it!" cried Adhemar of Puy, and those beside him took up the shout, which was reechoed in every corner of the wide field.

"God wills it!" cried Little Peter, his eyes misted over with a vision of the towers of Jerusalem, molten gold like the sun in the sky, the towers of Heaven.

Adhemar knelt before the Pope on the platform, asking permission to go. Gladly the Pope gave it as he proclaimed Adhemar the leader of the host. Joyfully he gave him a cross made of white silk to fasten on his mantle.

Others pressed forward to the platform, nobles first, their people following, and humbler men after that. Not all could mount the steps, but the Pope's attendants brought out baskets full of crosses in sign that their wearers were pledged to fight in the army of God. So great was the press of volunteers that the crosses were exhausted. People cut up the cloth laid over the platform, and its awning, and the cloaks of some who gave them to the cause. All colors these crosses were, silk or velvet, fine linen or rough homespun. Peter had one of ermine torn out of the lining of a rich nobleman's cloak. He held it in his hand because he had no brooch, but presently a housewife sewed it tight, sealing him into God's army. Thus marked with God's sign, Peter went forth to fix men's eyes on the golden towers of Heaven, as Our Lady had ordered.

PART I

The Dreamers

1096–1097

I⊤ was April, and the demesne had been plowed. The work had done little good for the peasants because the bailiff was a mean man who would sooner dismiss them at noon than give them dinner. There had been famine last year before the harvest, and there was want already. Women were out looking for dandelion leaves and grubbing up wild garlic. Crooked Jehan had taken his shoats to market to sell them for what they would fetch. It was best not to think what he could do, come Michaelmas, without them.

Alys looked for him at sundown, but the township was

far away, beyond the castle's lands and beyond the monastery's. She did not light a fire except on Sundays, so she gave
the boys some bread and suckled Bertha. They lay down
on the straw, but Alys felt cold without Jehan beside her.
She knew what he might do with aleshops handy and a
few coins in his purse. She wondered if she should have
sent Robert, too, or gone herself and left Bertha with the
boys.

Jehan came back in the early morning, meeting Alys with
Robert, the oldest boy, out gathering sticks.

"Never mind that, Alys," he told her. "We don't need a
fire any longer. We're going to Jerusalem. I came back to
fetch you."

"You're drunk," said Alys sullenly, facing disaster.

Jehan took no notice. His pale blue eyes were on the distant sun climbing above the horizon in molten glory. "Jerusalem," he said, "where the Lord God sits on a throne beside Saint Mary and everything shines gold. Rivers of milk
in the streets, Alys, and bread like fruit. No hunger ever."

"You're mad!" cried Alys, aghast.

"There was a man," said Jehan in his slow fashion, "a holy
man in a long cloak riding a donkey. He is taking us to
Jerusalem, and when we get there we shall all wear crowns
of gold and live like princes. You shall have a dress of pink
silk, Alys, like our lord's lady."

Alys wavered visibly. The tale was not improbable.
Everybody knew God lived in Heaven with Jesus and Mary
and Michael and all angels. She hadn't known that you
must journey to get there, but then perhaps the end of the

world was coming. She looked down at her dress of rough homespun, worked in, slept in, torn at the hem and patched at the knees. Slowly, as though she were not used to doing so, Alys smiled. "Blue," she said. "Blue like the Saints in church."

Jehan nodded. "Blue then," he said. "I shall wear green with fur on the edge."

If Jehan had had his way, they would have gone home for Bertha and Bartolf and set out on their road immediately. But Bertha could not walk far, and Alys said they must take with them the flour and the cooking pot. She expected that they might be days on the journey.

"We have to have a cart," she said decidedly.

Jehan was still lost in his thoughts, but he roused himself to shake his head. There was only the old sow to sell. The pennies which he had got for his shoats he had given to a beggar because he did not think he needed them. When Alys asked how he supposed they would live on the journey, he stroked his shaggy head in a puzzled way and said it did not matter. If they died, they would only get to Jerusalem faster. He pondered this a moment.

"It's better to see with your living eyes," he concluded.

The end of it was that they all set out for the market with Alys carrying Bertha, Jehan with the flour and the cooking pot, and the boys driving the sow along the road with switches. Alys and Jehan had rawhide shoes, but the children all went barefoot. They left no furnishings but the pig trough, a spade, a rake, a billhook, and a rope for binding faggots. What clothes they owned, they had on. It was a spring day, and the nights were growing warmer.

They meant to sell the sow, which was a good beast and farrowed well. They found themselves lost in a market in which peasants from ten miles round were selling too. Everybody wanted a cart, and nobody needed a pig, not even a good one. As for a donkey or an ox, one was not to be had.

Jehan hesitated, bringing his eyes down from the distant horizon with a sigh. Standing next them was a pedlar with a cart, a rickety object with two wheels, just big enough for the flour and the cooking pot and little Bertha if they squeezed in very tight. There was a dog to draw it, a great brindled creature, mainly mastiff. Jehan's vague eyes looked the equipage over, and suddenly he caught his breath. The dog was black of muzzle and quite dark, but on the front of him, on the barrel chest below the collar, he was marked with a white cross.

"My sow for your dog and cart," he said confidently, knowing that the Lord had set aside this creature for him.

The pedlar made haste to agree. The dog was stolen, and he had seen its owner in town a few minutes back. Jehan loaded the flour and the pot and the baby and set out leading the dog towards Jerusalem. It was afternoon.

Two hours later a wheel came off on a stone. Jehan had no tools to mend it, and in any case it needed blacksmith's work.

They sat by the side of the path and waited for the Lord to help them, while the children asked if Jerusalem was much farther. Presently an oxcart came over the brow of the hill with a red cross daubed upon it and a black-bearded peasant leading his beasts.

He halted when he got near and called to them. His name was Walther, and he was going to Jerusalem. His wife was in the cart and needed a woman.

Alys mounted the cart and went on her knees. She looked up angrily. "How like a man!" she said with contempt. "Could you not have waited a few days? Well, go get water in the pot. Jehan, make a fire."

When sunset came, there was another pilgrim, a little girl who screamed quite lustily as Alys laid her by her mother in the cart. Next morning they all went on together, the women riding with the children, and Jehan walking ahead with his dog on a rope.

Little Peter was moving towards Cologne and drawing after him an army which stripped the countryside like a horde of locusts. It is true that he had his wealthy supporters by now and traveled with a cart of silver pence to buy supplies. But whether or not men got a good price, they had little left for those who followed after, seeking to catch Peter up. Jehan's sack of flour was soon exhausted by the motley crowd which fell in behind him. It was a season of signs and wonders. Great cloud-palaces appeared in the sky. Comets fell. Devils were heard screeching in the woods at night, bewailing souls of sinners lost to them through the power of the Cross. Pious beggars displayed crosses traced upon their skins by heavenly angels. The sign upon Jehan's dog excited wonder in every village they entered. The power of God was on the beast, and it was noted that it went ahead of Jehan by a pace as though it led him.

Jehan walked in a dream, his pale eyes on the golden towers ahead. Walther came behind him, leading his oxen. Alys rode in the cart with Bertha and Margaret and the little girl. The boys did as they pleased, but mostly walked beside a donkey on which a juggler rode, a pious mountebank called Lambert who could whistle a merry tune, though he said the words were naughty and that he had taken a vow to sing no more such verses.

Lambert directed their path because he was a traveled man, steering them skilfully in a wide circle around the track of Peter's army. He set the boys begging in the villages in the name of the dog marked by a miracle. He christened the Company of the Dog and started to take tribute in the form of goods for the common store from those who desired to make the journey under holy protection. The company grew from a score to a hundred, and then to a hundred more, with a few pack animals, a herd of sheep, a goose or two, a tent for Lambert, and one for Jehan with the dog, and a purse of silver. If Jehan noticed how his train was growing, he paid no attention. He spoke little to anyone except to Alys.

"It is a long way to Jerusalem," said he one evening, "but it will not matter once we are there."

"Margaret's milk is drying up," said Alys.

Jehan made her no answer. He was snoring.

Alys took the child to her own breast and weaned little Bertha, while Margaret lay all day in the cart and hardly

moved. "I shall never get to Jerusalem," she murmured
one evening. Next morning she was cold and dead. Walther
sobbed over her body, but Jehan said she was already gone to
Jerusalem and they would meet her there. Alys wondered
how they would know her again, seeing that her earthly
body would be in the ground, they did not know precisely
where.

"She will know us," said Jehan with assurance. They
gave Margaret Christian burial in the nearest village, and
the priest christened the little girl, calling her Mary. By the
afternoon they were on their way, and on the next day
Walther was whistling to his beasts as usual.

Little Peter lay encamped outside Cologne with more people than they had supposed existed in the world. There
were breechless Scots from across the sea, Norse pirates,
Germans, Bretons, wild-looking men who spoke no language known. Whole villages had left their homes to follow
Peter, some sharing their provisions, some not, some sheltered from the rain by tents, some huddled under roofs of
sod or straw, some sleeping under carts. The noise of children, animals, or women could be heard a long way off,
and filth lay everywhere.

Little Peter moved through this crowd as ragged and dirty
as ever. The cross on his garment had lost half its fur, and
he had daubed it with a sheep-dip which gave it a reddish
color. When he approached, men knelt for his blessing as
to a saint. They struggled to get near him until the guards
about his donkey ran risk of being trampled. Tears rained
down bearded cheeks; horny hands were stretched towards

him. "Pray for me, Little Peter! Bless me! Remember me
in Heaven!"

Peter would put up his own hand, and a hush would fall.
He would tell them about the Saints they were going to
meet, the fine clothes they would wear, and the healing of
crooked limbs or failing eyes or loathsome sickness. He
would not hide from them that there was a long way to go
or that there might be hunger and savage beasts and wicked
men. Let each man arm himself with knife or pointed stick
or knotted club. God would be with them and bring them
to His promised land, though all the devils of Hell stood in
the way. Peter turned towards the rising sun; and men
turned with him, searching the horizon, below which lay
Jerusalem, the golden city of God.

Meanwhile, Peter appointed officers to go through the
camp and bid each family join together with some group.
There was bread for all because rich citizens of Cologne and
the cities round had given quantities of grain for the glory
of God. There was plenty of water, too, because the Rhine
is a fast-flowing river, so that the ordure and the beasts and
the washing of clothes did not pollute it.

There were many rough men in the camp but the dog
protected his company by his presence. None dared to provoke his growl, since God was with him. Alys kept close
to her tent, clucking after her children like an anxious
mother hen; but Robert and Bartolf were so spoiled by
weeks of idleness that she could not control them. Jehan,
lost in his dream, would hardly try. "People are wicked in
this world," he said, "but it will be different in Heaven."

"You must take a rope to Bartolf," Alys told him. "He slipped off when my back was turned, and this is no place for a seven-year-old to wander in." She found a rope for Jehan and made him promise to give the boy a thrashing; but when night fell, Bartolf did not come home.

Alys wanted to roam the camp calling wildly for her son, but Jehan held her tight and would not let her go. It was madness for a woman to be out at night. God would protect Bartolf and bring him to Heaven at last. This life did not matter.

Alys sobbed all night; and even Walther's new woman, who had lost a child herself, could not bring her comfort. In the morning Jehan went out to look, and Lambert went, and other men of the company; but Bartolf had dropped out of sight like a stone into deep water.

"God will keep him," Jehan said, but even he looked haggard, while Alys's face was lined like an old woman's.

Alys tied Bertha by a rope to her own girdle; and she made Jehan put a double rope on the dog so that he might hold one end and Robert the other on the march. Alys stopped talking about Bartolf, but she had a habit of scanning the crowds as though she might see him come into sight at any time. He never did.

Peter moved through Germany with his army while the meadows were yellow with cowslips and bluebells were out in the woods. It was holiday time for those used to toil and heavy burdens. The pace of marching was slowed by the children and cattle, and the Company of the Dog raised voices in hymns that Lambert taught them. The towns on their way were generous with bread, for they feared looting. Local peasants cursed when wheat was trampled or grazed down by the beasts, but Lambert said such people were well served for their greed. The Devil would get them because they had not dared to join the pilgrims. This being the case, it did no harm to take a fat goose if one could. The stews of the Company grew tasty as some of the men became accomplished thieves.

Things went less well when it rained. There was little shelter and never enough brush to use for bedding so that many slept on the wet ground. There was dysentry in the camp. Alys was coughing, and little Mary wailed incessantly. Jehan found her a nuisance and thought she would be best off with her mother in Jerusalem; but after Bartolf was lost, Alys had clung to Mary as though for comfort. Presently the trail of the army was marked by sick people falling out and even by bodies abandoned without so much as the rites of burial. But Peter still went ahead, and the dog led Jehan after.

By the time they reached Hungary, the men of the Company were no longer a rabble. Looting had led to skirmishing, which had shown the need for weapons. Pious men along the way had offered arms or armor for the good of their own souls, while many less pious had received the spiritual benefits of giving without their own consent. Occasionally there was blood upon such weapons. Lambert found a man-at-arms and made him drill the Company. Even Jehan had a sword, and he gave his knife to Alys in case she should need it.

There were fewer towns in Hungary, so that the bread which had been provided from vast ovens everywhere began to fail. The Company had not preserved its cattle when it saw how rich the land was through which they traveled. Even Walther's oxen had given out, so that they all had new shoes from them. Alys walked with the baby strapped to her back, while little Bertha was perched between the panniers of a donkey.

It was the custom of those parts to gather the grain into ricks, threshed only at need. These stood everywhere in the fields for the taking, and many rubbed out grain from the chaff to make a sort of porridge. This was laborious work and ill-done, so that the mess resulting was hardly eatable. Lambert got his men together and made a descent on a village to seize its threshing floor and beat out grain before the eyes of its proper owners.

All might have gone well, for the curses of the people were muttered in a barbarian tongue, while their weapons were no match for those of Lambert's men. It happened, however, that there was a strong beer brewed in those parts. What had started as a threshing party ended as a drunken brawl in which village girls were dragged away and village husbands were cracked on the head to keep them quiet. Stones came whizzing, one of which caught Lambert in the side and dropped him. Swords were drawn now, and scythes or billhooks snatched from cottages. Lambert's men withdrew, carrying their leader, leaving bodies in the street and houses blazing.

From this time on, the path of the army was marked by

pillars of smoke. Little Peter went around the camp preaching restraint, but Lambert said that holy men should leave
the fighting to those whose trade it was. Pilgrims were
killed every day, and it was necessary to set strong guards at
night lest bands of angry peasants take their vengeance.

Jehan would have shaken his head at Lambert's words;
but he was gone at that moment with the dog to find a priest,
since there was not one in the Company. Little Mary had
been taken with a convulsion and had turned blue. Presently she stopped breathing altogether. They could not bury
her in Christian ground, but the priest prayed over her
and said that she was surely with her mother. He was a
good man and questioned Jehan about the Company, which
had, he said, a poor reputation. Jehan opened his blue eyes
wide in surprise.

"They are all pilgrims to Jerusalem," he said.

The priest looked at Jehan and sighed. "Holy Peter is dis-
tressed because they murder Christian men."

Jehan looked blank, saying nothing because he was not
used to argument. As the army went on, however, he did
notice churches and a wayside cross or two, so that he discovered this was indeed a Christian land through which
they were passing. He said so to Lambert.

Lambert, in pain from two cracked ribs, was short with
Jehan. "You eat what we bring in, but you stay in camp
with the women," he snapped. "What do you or Little Peter
know about leading an army?"

Jehan would not eat that night, nor yet the next morning. Alys thought he was sick and pressed the food upon

him. Finally she wrung her hands. "If you fall by the way, what will happen to me and the children?"

Jehan turned this over in his mind. It had not occurred to him that he might not reach Jerusalem alive, nor had he wondered about Alys, seeing that they were all in the Lord's hand. But even his vague gaze had seen many sights in the army, and stories had come to his ears which he had not told Alys. He took the food from her hand and ate. After that, he used to look around for Alys and call her to his side when he remembered.

They crossed the river Save into Belgrade in a hurry. Belgrade was in the territory of the Emperor Alexius. By this time everyone knew that they were going to the city of Constantinople for rest and refreshment before they entered the land of the infidel. But the Emperor's forces had harried their crossing, attempting to keep them to one ford, so that there was fighting and massacre of prisoners. The pilgrims rolled into Belgrade, whose inhabitants had fled, and plundered it.

They left Belgrade burning. Alys had snatched a peasant's cloak to cover her rags, which were no longer decent. The army was again rich enough to buy its supplies. Partly for this reason, but also because the governor of the province had collected a considerable garrison, there was no trouble when they reached Nish. Little Peter gave hostages and paid good silver coins for flour. Great ovens were set up in the camp, and all the bakers of Nish came out to make the bread.

"Best get our own grain milled," Lambert said. At this

time the Company had several sacks of its own which were
carried on its donkeys. Lambert took men-at-arms and
rode off to the river to see to the business.

By now the army was setting out for Sofia, straggling as
usual over miles of highway. The women and children of
the Company of the Dog, who were waiting for Lambert,
looked anxious as the rearguard began to assemble.

A yelling broke out down by the river. Smoke arose from
the mills. The rear guard, surging about in no particular order, raised a shout of "Treachery!" Lambert came spurring
back with his sword bloody and sent a messenger up the
road to halt the march. The hotheads of the army, many of
whom looked up to Lambert, formed a knot about him,
ready to go to the rescue of his comrades. It could now be
seen that the mills were burning briskly, sending up great
flames into the sky. Knots of people were fighting along
the bank or falling back towards the camp. Lambert formed
up a squadron of cavalry, mounted on ponies, donkeys,
mules, or even cattle, and led a charge.

They rescued the Company of the Dog and might have
ended the fight by scattering the townsfolk. But the foot-
soldiers, who had long been murmuring against the leader-
ship of Holy Peter, had begun to yell they would teach the
men of Nish a lesson. Surging forward, they swept up to
the walls of the town, overrunning not merely those who
fled from the mills, but peaceful citizens who had ventured
out of the open gates to see what had happened.

So sudden was the attack that the east gate could not be
closed because of the people streaming back in panic. The

towers of the wall were not manned, save by a few watch-men; and frantic citizens got in the way of fighting men trying to assemble.

All was confusion in the town, but in the citadel the gover-nor had a force which he had recruited from the steppes of southern Russia. These were Turkish men on shaggy po-nies, dressed in sheepskins, bristling with short spears, and bows, and knives, all bred for war. These he sent out of another gate, whence they could circle to fall like thunder on the mob of pilgrims.

Now shrieks of terror arose. Men dropped their weapons and tried to run, but the main body had turned back to-wards Nish. Advancing to the rescue, it compressed the rear guard into a helpless mass in front of the Turks, who were soon red to the shoulders with blood and drunk with slaying.

Alys and Jehan were crouched behind a cart which served as a bulwark against the panic-stricken people, trampling each other as the maddened Turks pressed on them. Jehan had tied the dog to his belt. Alys was bent over Bertha to cover her with her body. Their frail shelter creaked and shifted under pressure.

One man dragged himself onto the cart and leaped for-ward onto the shoulders of the packed mass beyond. An-other followed, then another. Alys screamed. Jehan reached for her, but the rotten stuff of her dress tore in his hand. The weight of the crowd collapsed the cart, and Robert was swept away from his side. He snatched at Robert and caught him by the arm. The dog in a panic was scrabbling fran-

tically with his paws at people who, miraculously, shrank
away. Into this tiny breathing space Jehan was swept, while
Alys and Bertha went down beneath the feet of men to
reach Jerusalem before him.

Jehan glowered at the walls of Constantinople some weeks
later. The Queen of Cities shimmered in the hot, dry air,
and the smoke of its fires went up like the smoke of Hell.
The camp of the pilgrims was bigger than ever, despite its
losses at Nish; for other bands had by now converged, led
by other people. There were knights and horsemen among
these, though not very many, since the feudal lords were
gathering their forces slowly. Little Peter said they should
wait for the lords, but it seemed likely that the great ones
would delay till the end of the year. Jehan was impatient
because Alys was waiting in her blue robe by the golden
gate to see him come.

The Company of the Dog had changed its character since
Lambert had fallen with most of the men-at-arms at Nish.
Their women, if they survived the press, soon scattered to
seek new protectors. Strange stories, however, went around
about Jehan's escape. Men still hankered after signs and
wonders, even though the exposure of a thousand pious
frauds had made them cautious. Jehan, always turning his
eyes towards the horizon, was believed in because he made
no claims. Alms were thrust upon him, attracting the attention of the maimed, the sick, and the poor. This rabble
now hung about his heels, begging for him as well as for
themselves, and telling stories embroidered by Robert, who
had a turn for bragging.

Accustomed to hard labor, Jehan had found marching a holiday; but it irked him to sit in a dusty camp in the boiling heat doing nothing. Many in a similar state of mind relieved their feelings by picking quarrels with the townsfolk, or by stealing. Daily the Emperor Alexius remonstrated with Peter and the other leaders, who contented themselves with blaming one another.

Jehan went up the ridge with his dog beside him to get a view of the Golden Horn, the famous harbor through which poured all the wealth of the East. Such a forest of shipping lay there that all the pilgrims, many thousands though they were, might have been taken with their animals and their gear across the straits. But the Emperor counseled them to wait, and Little Peter said they must have patience. Jehan sighed.

The dog twitched the rope out of Jehan's hand and was away after a rabbit. A flock of sheep went into a silly panic and scattered in front of him with foolish baaings. Their shepherd gave a warning shout and whizzed a stone which hit the animal and bowled him over. He did not get up, and the shepherd ran towards him with iron-tipped staff upraised to finish him off.

Jehan raced through the pasture to stand across his dog, drawn sword in hand. The shepherd whistled to friends, while Jehan shouted to pilgrims who had strayed along the ridge and now came running to him. The ill-will, which had been brewing for many a day, now broke into a fight in which the pilgrims, being better armed, had the advantage. They drove the shepherds down the hill, leaving

Jehan bent over his dog to feel its leg, which was broken.

There were villas lining the Golden Horn outside the city into which rich men retired in summertime to get sea breezes. Isaac Comnenus, the Emperor's brother, to whom the sheep and the pasture and most of the hillside belonged, was aroused by the clash of weapons and came out as he was, in silken garments, but with a sword which he had snatched up in his hand. When he saw what was going on, he shouted loudly for his bodyguard. Meanwhile, advancing boldly, he yelled out to the Franks in their own language to surrender.

None of the pilgrims knew his name, but it was not difficult to guess that they had angered a powerful lord. If they were taken, it seemed most likely they would be hanged. Used as they were to looting and disorder, it did not take them long to kindle the gorse on the hillside to cover their escape. The season was July, and everything was dry as tinder. Fanned by a hot little breeze, the fire swept down on the villa.

The patience of the Emperor Alexius was exhausted when his brother reported to him what had been done. Disorderly masses were no use to the Emperor and would be very little to their own lords when these should arrive. In the meantime, they did not respect his royal name, the palace of his brother, or even the churches of the blessed Saints. They were stealing lead from the church roofs in the neighborhood of their encampment.

"Let them go," said the Emperor in exasperation. "Let them plunder the Turk across the straits and take their chance." All the same, he impressed upon Peter, whom he thought wiser than the rest, that the rabble should hold a fortified place until spring. There was an old camp in a place called Civetot which lay on the seashore of Asia Minor, handy for supplies from Constantinople.

Civetot was crowded and dusty. Jehan worked on repairing the walls and liked the labor because it was something to do. He could not understand why they halted, since Little Peter had promised God would protect them from the infidel. It was perfectly simple to march, one foot before the other, drawing nearer with every step not only to Alys, but to the Mother of God, the golden gates, and all the angels. Jehan did not speak of this except to Robert, and even to him he only muttered, "It is easy to go on."

Inwardly, Jehan hated the camp of Civetot, which looked west to the sea and was cut off from the eastward by a line of hills. Nothing was talked of there but chance of plunder, especially after a few thousands ventured to make a raid and got back heavily laden. Jehan sat gloomily by while drunken tales were told of torturing captives or roasting babies alive over the campfires.

Little Peter left in disgust and went back to Constantinople. Men had shouted him down when he tried to preach, and even Jehan no longer trusted him. After having brought them halfway across the world, he would not lead them against the infidel. Spring was half a year away. Last April Alys and Jehan had set out together, and now she was wondering why he did not come.

Confusion increased in the camp. Some said that a de-

tachment of Germans had captured Nicaea, richest city of
those parts and inexhaustible in plunder. They wanted to
set out and share the loot. Others said that a Turkish force
was marching against them and that they should go out
and smite it in the name of the Holy Cross. After a great
deal of clamor from both factions, it was agreed that fighting men should march on the following morning, leaving
women and children, invalids and cowards in Civetot until
the battles were over.

They mustered in irregular bands, twenty thousand more
or less. Perhaps a score of knights rode at the head in full
armor with the mounted men-at-arms, a hundred or more.
Next came the companies which had drilled themselves for
fighting. After these followed light-armed men, and at the
tail came rabble escorting donkeys laden with provisions.

Jehan set out, blissful with happiness, simply because
they were once more marching east. Someone had given
him a leather cap and jerkin, and he had his sword slung
by a rope across his shoulder. It was familiar to him now,
though for a while it had been too long and clumsy for him
to use. He walked with the rabble because he had no
fighting Company at his heels. Even Robert was left behind
in the care of Walther, who had suffered a sword-thrust in
the arm which had disabled him from fighting.

It was a clear October day, and spirits were high. Those
riding in the van were playing with their swords, throwing
them in the air and catching them. The companies were
singing tunes which, originally pious, had degenerated by
now into bawdy verses.

Their way led through a pass in the hills no more than three miles outside Civetot. No sooner were they well inside the gap, straggling as usual, when Turks appeared on the hills before and behind. They let fly with arrows in great numbers, unhorsing the armored men in the front and speedily throwing the irregular companies into a panic. The rabble in the rear, not all completely surrounded, broke and fled. After them pounded mounted Turks, and the slaughter began.

Men died in every conceivable way in the pass or on the plain. Hardly a thousand survived that day, to be rescued by the ships of the Emperor and brought back to Constantinople. Amid the panic-stricken mobs on the plain, the Turks encountered a little bandy-legged man with a crooked shoulder with a dog in front of him, still plodding steadily towards the East. They opened their ranks and let him go, for they respected people whom the hand of Allah clearly touched with madness. Jehan advanced into the pass where volleys of arrows rained down on the stricken mass entrapped within.

An arrow hit the dog, who fell, writhing and biting at the weapon in his flank. Jehan bent over him. An arrow transfixed him in the back, and he collapsed forward, his dying eyes still trying to look eastward. At that same instant, the Turks broke into Civetot and began to massacre there. There Walther perished with all the sick and the maimed, but boys like Robert were set aside for slaves. A few days later they were moved east past the bodies of their men and disappeared from Christian sight forever.

Thus ended Little Peter's crusade, but he himself came that way in the spring riding his donkey with the great lords and their army. Bones whitened the plain and vast mounds of skulls had been piled up for counting. The army reestablished itself in Civetot, rebuilding its walls in stone and grinding the bones to make mortar with them, or piling them between the stones for rubble. In this way Jehan and his dog watched over the pilgrims who still came streaming from the west towards Jerusalem. Little Peter went on with these to the fulfillment of his dream.

The Conquerors

1096–1099

Rᴏʙᴇʀᴛ ᴏғ Sᴀɪɴᴛ Aᴠᴏʟᴅ was the biggest knight in Lorraine. It was the custom in that Duchy for ambitious young men to prove themselves by challenging all comers to joust with them near the chapel of Saint George. Half the knights of the Duchy had fought in that place with varying fortunes, but Robert of Saint Avold had never done so. For three days he had lingered, dedicating his arms to Saint George and promising a silver candlestick which he could ill afford, but to no purpose. No one had the foolhardiness to ride against him.

Robert swaggered about this episode, sweeping beer foam off his vast moustaches in a gesture which concealed uneasiness. As a landless younger son, he had to make his fortune by the strength of his right arm. He was sensible enough to see that a bloodless victory led nowhere.

When Godfrey of Bouillon, Duke of Lower Lorraine, took the Cross, he sent for Robert, who was a distant cousin of his, and offered a place among his retinue of knights. As a tall man himself, Godfrey did not fear comparison with the enormous outlines of his vassal. On the contrary, he was glad to be attended by such an impressive soldier.

Robert almost wept with joy. One whole night he knelt in Godfrey's chapel, pouring out his heart to Saint Martin, also a soldier. He was bursting with love of adventure, desire to prove his worth, and need to win his place amid the great ones. Never had he hoped that all this would be offered in the army of God and His Saints, so that by doing what he most wished on earth, he might also win Heaven. Eagerly he made a solemn vow to Saint Martin that he would charge the infidel ahead of all other gallant knights in the army. Next morning he confessed and was shriven of his sins before he took the Cross, so that he might be worthy of the honor. Some months later, at a time when Little Peter had already reached Constantinople, Robert of Saint Avold rode joyfully out behind his lord to seek his fortune.

There were many signs and wonders on the journey in evidence that God was with them. Robert did not expect the Saints to grant him a vision when there were so many godly priests to receive them. But the dreams of others fortified faith, and he saw shooting stars or cloud formations which people said were companies of angels. It was glorious to be riding in God's army towards the end of earthly bliss, His Holy City.

The power of the Cross did not lessen the task of commanding an expedition. It was not long before the knights in his attendance had taken the measure of their overlord. The Duke of Lorraine was a pious Christian knight, tall, yellow-haired and handsome, but no real leader of men. He wished other people to know his mind before he understood it himself; but at the same time he was jealous, as weak men are, of his authority. He preferred his followers a little stupid and took a fancy to Robert of Saint Avold because his size, his booming voice, and his good humor made him appear thick-headed. Robert was eager to serve, and he responded with a devotion which was not affected by Godfrey's personal failings. Indeed, he felt protective of his lord, and never more so than when the army arrived at Constantinople.

None of them liked the Easterners. "Why should they look superior?" complained Robert to Gilbert of Tournai, who was one of the young knights in Godfrey's company. "They were not men enough to defend God's land from the infidel, and I do not wonder at it now I see them." He stood at the corner of Mese Street and the Square of the Bull, glowering at a wheeled carriage attended by turbaned men on foot and containing a painted woman who had stared at him haughtily as her equipage brushed past. "Should I give place to that?" He squared his shoulders, standing like a great rock around which all the traffic of the busy hour of the day must swirl and divide.

Gilbert of Tournai was looking resentfully up the colonnade of Mese Street where dark shops held wares inviting plunder. "With half a company at my back, I'd make these merchants skip!" He put a hand on his sword with a truculent gesture which made a little man dodge nervously round him. Gilbert laughed and spat at his feet.

"You'd not do that at court," grumbled Robert, expanding his grievance to include the Emperor Alexius, whose gold brocade and scarlet shoes and glittering jewels had made a poor impression. "They're all so high and haughty that it's embarrassing so much as to clear your throat. But when it comes to supplies, pack animals, siege engines, guides, or shipping, nothing's ready. They asked us, didn't they?" He brooded angrily.

The Emperor was smooth. He was even lavish with rich gifts for Duke Godfrey and his vassals. Supplies came slowly, however, and ships were promised for some vague time in the future. When Godfrey clumsily tried to use his army to force terms, the Emperor withheld food altogether and brought up his mercenaries to defend the city. Godfrey was forced to give in and pay Alexius homage as overlord of all the lands which he might conquer.

The army chafed at the delay. In imagination men were already winning fabulous glory. In no time at all they would with God's aid be in the Holy City, where Robert vowed to light a candle before the Sepulchre. Others thought him too modest.

"A tenth of our pagan spoils to the City of God!" cried Hugo Grossetete, his little eyes kindling at the thought of uncounted riches.

"And a tenth of the spoils of Constantinople!" added Gilbert of Tournai, drunken on Greek wine.

The sally was greeted with a roar of approval. Men had been looting in the suburbs to such an extent that they had set up a market in camp to sell goods back to their original owners. Some purses were full of gold besants, but many discovered that the townsfolk rapidly cheated them out of their gains. "Thieving rascals!" muttered Hugo Grossetete, refilling the silver cup which he had stolen from the chapel of Saint Barnabas nearby.

None was more eager for the barbarians to be gone than the Emperor himself, but he had determined that the great vassals must first be forced to pay him homage. They were going to conquer lands which had once been his, and he must establish his overlordship now or never. It would be hard for Godfrey's vassals to refuse an oath their lord had sworn.

The lords of the army submitted with resentment. They dared no longer delay because their men were saying that they would either go on or take ship for home. Choking with fury, Godfrey's vassals swore fealty to Alexius on their knees.

In return, the Emperor was very gracious. With a cour-

tesy he would not have paid to his own subjects, he got up
from his throne when the homage was over and advanced
to meet Duke Godfrey and his brother, Count Baldwin.

Robert of Saint Avold looked at his lord's high color and
at the black brows of his vassals standing awkwardly
bunched, while the courtiers in their silk gowns ignored
them. Something had to be done, and he thought that he
would do it.

"Watch me!" he muttered through his moustaches to Gilbert of Tournai. Strolling forward, he went up the steps
of the throne and sat on it.

An audible gasp was followed by a shocked silence in
which the courtiers stared straight in front of them, deliberately not seeing. Alexius himself, aware from the expression upon Duke Godfrey's face that something had happened, turned to behold the huge Frank in his seat. Raising
his eyebrows very slightly, he stood waiting.

Duke Godfrey was at a loss for words, but his brother
Baldwin, as dark as he was fair, had a readier wit. "Get up
for shame!" he said sharply. "You are the Emperor's liege
man, yet you insult him!"

Robert glanced at Godfrey and decided he had pleased
him. He grinned stupidly. "Why should one man sit while
the rest of us stand?" He stretched out his legs and put his
arms along those of the throne, thinking privately that he
filled it better than Alexius.

"It is the custom of the country," Baldwin said. "Get
up!" His voice was curt.

Robert got up. He dared not argue further with Count

Baldwin, and besides he had gained his end. The ceremonial had been upset, and not quite everything had gone the Easterners' way. He was taken by surprise when a courtier tapped him on the shoulder and escorted him to where the Emperor stood. Alexius was calmly curious about his bad manners, and Robert lacked the assurance to tell him what he thought. He took refuge in bluster, stammering that he was a warrior good as any man and had taken a vow to prove it on the Turks. Why, at the chapel of Saint George in his own country . . . He swept his moustaches with the familiar gesture and cleared his throat.

Alexius heard him to the end, smiling at him in the disdainful way these Easterners had and managing in spite of his dwarfish height to look Robert up and down in contemptuous fashion. "If you are eager for fighting, why, the Turks will oblige you." He turned his back. Robert felt like a fool as it occurred to him for the first time that Alexius had fought in many battles.

Godfrey said nothing about this incident; but other people toasted Robert, who found himself a famous man. His popularity went to his head, especially as his vow brought others into fashion. A body of young knights soon swore to follow him whenever he might charge into the thick of the battle.

Still more time passed while other armies, coming by sea or land gathered under Raymond, Count of Toulouse, Hugh, brother of King Philip, Bohemond the Norman, Bishop Adhemar of Puy, and various others. Unluckily for Robert's vow, when the combined army finally set out through Asia Minor, they found the fighting different from their expectations. Turks did not charge into battle like Christian men, but preferred to wheel on the flanks in squadrons, discharging arrows and retiring to give place to others when their quivers were empty. Lightly armed and mounted on tough little ponies, they were difficult to catch, especially as the knights in their heavy armor rode horses of a huge and clumsy build. Robert and his followers looked foolish as skirmishes went by, Nicaea was taken, and the Sultan was repulsed without one chance of fulfilling their vows.

Their opportunity came unexpectedly. To ease the problem of supplies, the army was marching in two divisions. Its vanguard was surprised by a Turkish army lying in ambush on the hillsides around the plain of Dorylaeum. Bohemond the Norman, who was in command, was quick to send back a messenger to warn the rest to hurry to the rescue. Then he formed his men in a circle around the women, priests, and noncombatants whom they had with them, ordering all to stand on the defensive.

There was nothing to do for several hours but endure the rain of arrows and the heat of the burning sun. A good many Christians had bows, but these were inferior to the weapons of the Turks, who were easily able to shoot into the Christian ranks from a safe distance. Women and unarmed men, who were at first busy bringing water to the soldiers, were soon huddled under carts or extra shields for what protection they could get. Meanwhile, the Christians had shot their quivers empty, for they regarded bows as mere skir-

mishing weapons and did not carry much ammunition with
them.

Robert stirred impatiently in his saddle. "We ought to
teach them not to come so close!"

His neighbor looked grim. "If we could catch them."

Unpunished, the Turkish squadrons ventured nearer.
Men-at-arms protected only by leather jerkins were suffering severely. Even chain mail showed its weak links when
arrows whistled sharply from a short distance off. Horses
crashed snorting to the ground. Women screamed. Churchmen fell on their knees, commending the army loudly to
God's pity.

Robert's neighbor lifted a hand to brush away a fly, and
an arrow transfixed him under the arm through a gap in
his armor. He slid off his horse with a clash of chain mail.
All around him, men were looking about for somewhere to
take refuge.

Robert rose in his stirrups and lifted his spear. "Come
on! Follow me! We'll teach them a lesson!" He touched
his spurs to his horse and, closely followed by a mob
of younger knights, swept yelling forward.

Too late the Turkish squadron tried to scatter. Robert
fell on it like a thunderbolt, huge horse and massive rider
bursting deep into the ranks of unarmored horsemen whose
swords were too light to pierce his stout chain mail. His
spear was wrenched from his hand, deep in the body of a
dying man trampled under his horse's hooves. He snatched
out his sword. Behind him, the other knights were howling
like demons. Rolled together in a confused mass of armored

knights and fleeing bowmen, they surged across the plain, leaving men behind them dead or dying.

The rise of the ground saved the Turks. Robert's horse slackened his pace, exhausted by the weight of his master wearing body armor. The light-armed Turks drew off on their hardy ponies, leaving the knights clustered at the foot of the slope. Now arrows attacked them from squadrons to the right and left, which were pressing forward to cut off their retreat to the Christian army.

Robert swung his horse around. His charge had been glorious, and he thought the enemy would be careful not to venture so close for the future. Meanwhile, he must lead his men back before they were shot down. Already there was a wound in his thigh. His horse felt slippery with blood. He spurred it into a lumbering trot, shouting to the others to follow.

Horse after horse went down as they recrossed the plain. The Turks were shooting low. When a man was once dismounted, they pursued him with a storm of arrows till he dropped. The rest of the knights crouched in their saddles, grimly enduring.

Robert's horse stumbled and fell. He was on foot with arrows clanging on his shield or against his helmet, making him stagger. He was retreating backward, presenting his armored front and shield to the foe; but if he stumbled over stick or stone he would never get up. There was an arrow in his side, and his armor chafed it, making it agony to move. He dared not wrench out the barb, lest his lifeblood follow with it. Where else he was wounded he did not know or care. He was still able to grip his sword and shield, so that the enemy, circling like a wheeling flock of vultures, did not close.

"Let the fool die!" raged Bohemond when some of his knights asked him if they might not charge out to rescue Robert. "Did I not order all men to stand fast in their ranks, and has he not cost us a score of knights at least? Let no man stir from his place, lest he reckon with Bohemond the Norman."

Robert sank to his knees, propping his shield on the ground and crouching behind it. None of the Turks would come any closer, suspecting they were being drawn into a trap. It was hardly worth their while to shoot at Robert now. They turned their arrows on the Christian ranks, but these had been heartened by the respite. A rumor had begun to spread that the rest of the army was arriving.

Its appearance caught the Turks by surprise, since they had imagined that all the Christians were inside their trap. Now they themselves were entrapped by Adhemar of Puy, who had led a detachment along the ridge to take them in the rear. They broke and fled in such haste that they left their tents behind, even including the silken tent of their Sultan and his treasure.

Robert of Saint Avold was found to be still living by his grooms, who had rushed forward to carry him out of the battle. He had lost so much blood and was wounded in so many places that they were certain he would die.

"It's what the fool deserves," said Bohemond sharply.

Many agreed with the Norman, angry at the death of a

cousin or liegeman who had charged behind Robert and gone down under the arrows. Godfrey, as usual swayed by stronger men, looked sullen when Robert's name was mentioned and would not so much as go to see how he did. But Adhemar of Puy had talked to Bohemond's chaplain and learned that the army had been on the edge of panic. If the men-at-arms had fled or tried to take shelter, they would all have been massacred. Adhemar suspected that Robert's charge had been timely, though he did not wish to provoke a quarrel with Bohemond. He merely remarked that the soldiers of God were not so numerous that they could afford to lose a stalwart knight. The Emperor Alexius had attached a physician to his own train who had lived many years in Saracen lands and had learned their secrets of healing. He would carry Robert among his men, so that Theodore might attend him.

Days passed while the army moved on with its wounded in litters, not daring to leave them behind in a hostile land. Robert of Saint Avold hardly knew where he was, for he was in agony from the ribs that had been shattered by the arrow in his side. He who a while before had been the strongest knight in the army was so weakened by loss of blood that he could not lift his head. In half-lucid moments, he thought he was in a bad dream because he saw no one about him but a man called Theodore, clad in eastern garments and with a hawklike nose and sallow face. Theodore laid cooling things on his wounds and made him swallow a bitter medicine. Presently he began to realize that Theodore was not a dream.

"Am I a prisoner?" he murmured.

Theodore smiled reassuringly. "You are traveling in the suite of the Bishop of Puy. In a few weeks we shall reach Antioch, which is the gateway to Syria and the Holy Land. There you may rest and gain your strength, for the siege of a great town like Antioch will take time."

"In the bishop's suite?" Robert frowned, feebly puzzled. "My lord Godfrey?"

"Is well."

Robert closed his eyes and drifted back into his dreamlike state. But after a hideous day of being jolted as the donkeys carrying his litter trotted up rocky paths and round precipitous ledges, he seemed more wide awake. When his grooms carried him into his tent, they noticed that his cheeks, lately so pale, had a small spot of color. As they laid him down, he clutched one by the tunic and began to ask him questions. Later, when Theodore came with his evening draught of medicine, he turned his head away.

"Better be dead than disgraced," he muttered sourly.

"Your men are fools," retorted Theodore. "There is no question of disgrace."

"None came to see me, even my lord Godfrey."

"The knights have their own trouble in this weather."

This was certainly true because rain fell heavily so that even the litter, though protected by a canopy, was sodden. Robert coughed and hurt his side, and coughed again. It was the sort of weather in which armor rusted and bowstrings snapped. Horses caught cold and died. Some of the knights were riding on donkeys, and even occasionally on cattle. Men who slept in the mud would awake too cramped to walk.

Robert of Saint Avold was soon in a high fever. The wound in his side was festering, and pieces of bone were coming out with the pus. He thought they must be near Jerusalem, and he kept talking of the candle which he had promised to the Sepulchre. Theodore moistened his parched lips, but he would not try to swallow, so that medicine ran out of the corners of his mouth.

"Best fetch a priest before he dies," said the groom in attendance.

Theodore stroked his long nose in a thoughtful gesture. "It is a pity to lose so young a man." He took Robert by the hand and bent right over him, bringing his own face into the light of the taper which stood behind the head of the bed. "Go to sleep, Robert, or you will not be strong enough to enter the city."

Robert looked at him, wide-eyed, restless, half taking in what was said and half arrested by the calm command of his tone. His eyes met Theodore's and seemed to focus on them. "Jerusalem! I said I would offer a candle — !"

"If you will go to sleep, you shall do so," Theodore promised.

Gray eyes glittering in a sunken face looked into black ones. "Go to sleep," ordered Theodore quietly.

"Sleep — "

Theodore put down the bony hand which he had been holding on top of the fine blue coverlet given by Adhemar. "You may go to bed," he said to the groom without turning. "I shall watch by him tonight and do what he needs."

Robert opened his eyes in the gray of the next morning before the trumpets had wakened the bustle of the army. He smiled mistily at Theodore, who was bending over him. "We went into Jerusalem through the Jaffa Gate. We were riding donkeys through the streets, and we stabled them . . . we stabled . . . There was a door with a grille which opened to us, and a court . . . I don't remember."

"Never mind the court," Theodore said quickly. There was a tinge of red in his sallow cheek. "Remember the church of the Sepulchre instead."

"I offered a candle," said Robert dreamily. "There were so many candles! Incense was burning in front of the True Cross. Black monks were chanting, so that in the Sepulchre music sounded like songs from Paradise."

"Remember it well!"

The morning trumpets began to blare, and Robert started. Pain stabbed him in the side, and he blinked uneasily. "Where are we?"

"In the Taurus mountains going down to Syria, a week or so away from Antioch."

"But we rode through the streets of Jerusalem. I saw them! Was I out of my senses?"

Theodore took his hand and began to feel his pulse. "You are not out of them now, for your fever is less. Perhaps God granted you a vision."

Robert stared at him, round-eyed. "I, Robert of Saint Avold saw a vision! It is not possible!"

Theodore shrugged with a smile. "Perhaps it was a pity

that so fine a young man should die. Who knows how
God may feel about His servants?"

Robert looked at him suspiciously. The Devil also had his
magic and was cunning to entrap men in his snare. "Did
not you and I ride through the streets and stable our donkeys? Why did you guide me through Jerusalem?"

Theodore met his gaze blandly. "I think you do not remember how it was. God does not need to show me Jerusalem in a dream, for I was born there."

The army moved into the Syrian plain and came to Antioch, which was a fair city almost as great as Constantinople. They encamped around it more or less, for part of its
wall lay along the river and part across a mountaintop, so
that they could not get near it. Robert lay propped in his
tent and talked to Theodore about Jerusalem, where it
seemed there were many Christians, some heretic and others
of the Greek persuasion. Theodore's brother lived there
still and was a merchant respected by the Saracens, for
many of the infidel had friends among the Greeks.

Robert listened, often shocked and occasionally fearful
lest Theodore and his brother be sons of the Devil. Cautiously he fingered the Missal which Bishop Adhemar had
sent him when he heard that God had granted him a dream.
He even opened it and ran his hand across the pages to
touch the Latin which he could not read. But either the
holy words ought to be pronounced, or Theodore was truly
a man of God, since he did not make horrible faces and
disappear.

"You are restless for lack of something to do," said Theo-

dore. He smiled. "I imagine you have never lain still for a
day in your life and have no notion what you may do with
your time. Why do you not learn the Arabian tongue? I
will send you a teacher."

Robert's mouth dropped open, and he felt for his moustaches as though uncertain that they were still on his lip.

"Bohemond the Norman speaks it, and Count Baldwin
has a teacher in his train, for these are people who desire to
win lordships in the East and make their homes here."
Theodore considered. "I will find you eastern garments,
though for your size it is not easy. You cannot bear the tightness of your own clothes yet."

He took his leave, and for a long time Robert lay quiet,
staring at the flies which circled the tent and rubbing his
fingers across his lips with a puzzled expression.

A month went by, and then another. The siege of
Antioch showed no sign of coming to an end because the
army could neither take the town nor leave so great a city
lying unsubdued in their rear. Robert of Saint Avold was
beginning to walk again and came across old comrades who
greeted him warmly. So much marching and fighting had
gone on since the battle of Dorylaeum that they expressed
a crude surprise to find him living. They guffawed loudly
at his eastern garments and clapped him on the shoulder,
sending him reeling, until he was glad to get back to his
tent and sit down.

Those in the train of Adhemar of Puy were easier to talk
to. The bishop led fighting men as well as priests, but his
warriors were generally older people. They were anxious

to question Robert about his vision, which he could not clearly remember any more. They told him also that there was rivalry between Bohemond the Norman and Raymond, Count of Toulouse, the former demanding the lordship of Antioch, while the latter supported the Emperor's claim. Godfrey of Bouillon swayed to one side and then the other, influenced by his brother Count Baldwin, who had already left the army to establish himself in the northeast as lord of Edessa. The wise ones in Adhemar's train thought that the rest of the army would break up in the same way, were it not for the bishop.

"Queer thing about Robert of Saint Avold," remarked Gilbert of Tournai almost a year later. "Never really the same since he was wounded." He licked his fingers and wiped them carefully on his bread. "Pity," he added.

Hugo Grossetete champed steadily on a piece of gristle, taking time to empty his mouth enough to answer. "Should have thought myself," he said at last, "that Robert was bigger than ever."

"Daresay he is," admitted Gilbert. He reflected on the matter. "Daresay he isn't though, because if I remember the size he always was, he couldn't be bigger. Never saw such a man since I was born. It's a pleasure to watch him in battle with a mace in his hand."

Hugo Grossetete took out the rest of his morsel between thumb and forefinger and threw it on the floor. He blinked his little eyes, absorbed in a mental picture of Robert dashing out infidel brains and covered with gore.

Duke Godfrey's attendants offered water and a napkin

for the cleansing of greasy fingers. The Duke was finicky in
his ways, even on the march.

"It's not his strength I mean," pursued Gilbert. "But he
talks to everybody Greek or Saracen! Never know who
you'll find in his tent. In fact, better not know." He made
the sign of the Cross. Hugo stared at him in alarm.

"You can't possibly mean — "

"Of course I don't," snapped Gilbert. "It's queer, that's
all. His servants say that doctor of the bishop's put a spell
on Robert. He called himself Christian, that man, but only
a Greek. Nobody liked him."

Hugo shook his head, dismayed. Travel had taught him
that Christians of other sects were in league with the Devil.

"Whatever happened to that cursed fellow?" he inquired.

"Went back to the Emperor when Bishop Adhemar died.
God rest his soul!" He crossed himself in memory of
Bishop Adhemar, whose untimely death of fever had been
followed by quarreling among the leaders. Indeed, it was
only recently that Godfrey with Raymond of Toulouse and
the bulk of the army had turned their way towards Jerusalem at last.

It was true that Robert was talking to all sorts of people.
There were infidel prisoners of high rank awaiting ransom,
and others came in to surrender citadels. Greek-speaking
Christians were sent by the towns or nearby villages to
negotiate the sale of supplies. Traders flocked in, buying
plunder or selling the eastern spices, silken robes, and other
luxuries which were transforming the comfort of the army.
Two years had passed since Robert had set out with Godfrey,

dazzled by the excitement of war and blood and glory. He had sat on an emperor's throne without considering that government is an art. By now he had learned many things which he had not then known. Yet he was still a warrior vowed to God, in Whose service it was glorious to slay the infidel. The goal was Jerusalem, of which God Himself had granted him a vision.

Twelve miles from Jerusalem the pilgrim army had its first sight of the city of God, built high in the hills and surrounded by the usual wall and towers. To Little Peter, who was with them still, the sunlit town was gilded with God's glory. He felt the presence of the unseen angels of Heaven, of the ranks of all the Saints, of the spirits of those martyrs whose white bones mouldered on a distant plain or stiffened the ramparts of a long-deserted crusader camp on the Bosporus shores. Little Peter fell on his knees and stretched out his arms. Robert did so likewise, vainly trying to recall the Jaffa Gate of his dream or to imagine the dusty streets of the living town where God Himself once walked. Tears trickled down Hugo Grossetete's cheek, scarred by an arrow wound and set in hard lines by deeds of brutality against both infidel and native Christian. Even to Hugo, Jerusalem held the secret of heavenly bliss and the delivery from all the countless ills that flesh is heir to. Gilbert of Tournai touched the Cross he wore on his shoulder, thinking of the wife and child he had left for God and to whom, once his vow was accomplished, he longed to return. Here lay the end of two whole years of separation. Duke Godfrey bowed himself to the very ground and kissed the earth.

One might suppose it would be an anticlimax to surround those dusty walls, look for wood to build siege engines, and settle down to the dullness of encampment. Men felt themselves, however, in the presence of God, so that even those routines were hallowed. Signs and wonders, which had in the past months been the subject of coarse jests, revived once more. Around their campfires, the knights boasted of what they would accomplish for God, Robert among them. Great grace had been given the army, and it would be sin to spare the infidel. Plunder, too, was part of the trade of arms; and the glorious gamble which might make a man rich for life aroused a fever of expectation. Many were ready to claw their way up the battlements before the mangonels, the sappers, and the siege towers did their work. God would be with them!

Five weeks later, maddened by heat, enraged by losses brought on by rash assaults, alarmed by the rumor of a vast relieving army setting out from Egypt, most were in a desperate mood. Some even now deserted the pilgrimage, maintaining that since they had reached the Holy City, they had fulfilled their vow to God. Others blamed the leaders for sinful quarreling about who should become king of God's own town.

God came to the aid of his faithful, sending a message through Bishop Adhemar, who appeared to a holy man in a dream and told him that after a three-day fast they should go in procession around the walls, as Joshua once did about Jericho. Then let them make their assault and take the city.

The words of the good bishop kindled hope. The procession which went around Jerusalem was deeply in earnest. Men walked barefoot, joining in the singing of the priests who carried crosses high before them. From the walls the infidel soldiers looked down and laughed.

"Kill the blasphemous dogs!" muttered Hugo Grossetete, interrupting his chant with a curse. "Wash the whole city clean with blood! Let no foul pagan live who has defiled it!"

"They have driven all the Christians out," Gilbert agreed, "save only a few who are as good as pagans. There are none others within the walls except the Moslems and the accursed Jews. It would be a great sin to spare any of these."

Duke Godfrey was more concerned about the plunder. Never a rich lord, he had not prospered in the Crusade, since his lack of resolution made him no match for other greedier men. As usual, however, Duke Godfrey could not control his knights.

"Each for himself!" was the general cry. "Let every man mark down a house to enter and hang his shield on the wall. Inside, let him plunder and slay to his heart's content. No man need dispute his prize, for all is ours." Had not Pope Urban himself promised them the spoils, reflecting doubtless that the laborer is worthy of his hire? Far off in Rome, while the army girded on its mail for battle, Pope Urban, who had sent them out, lay dying.

By now Duke Godfrey's men had built a siege tower on wheels the height of the city wall and containing a landing bridge to let down onto it. Before this could be used, they must fill in the moat. Godfrey gave orders that the mangonels have fresh piles of stones for ammunition and that the women and unarmed folk be given spades and made to labor filling sacks of earth to be cast into the ditch. Then seizing the first sack, he gave the signal by running forward to the moat's edge and hurling it in.

It was nighttime when the work began, but the stars were out and the besieged had torches flaring at intervals along the wall so that sentries might see movement. Almost immediately their horns were blowing the alarm and men were gathering on the wall from nearby towers. A storm of arrows laid half a score of the assailants low and daunted others who were running up with their sacks towards the moat. With a whirr and a crash the first of Godfrey's mangonels let fly an ill-aimed missile which rebounded from the wall and fell into the moat.

"Bring up the mantlets!" someone yelled. Groups of men detailed for the task were already trundling wheeled shelters across the rough ground to the moat so as to give protection to the men coming up with their sacks. Only for a moment did these need to appear on the edge of the moat and cast in their burdens. One man dared it and leaped back into shelter unhurt. The next man fell with a scream into the moat, already half buried by the bursting of his sack on top of his body.

Now the mangonels of the besieged began to play, thudding haphazard here and there, but doing damage to the mantlet screen which had to be reinforced by bags of earth so that for a long space no more fell into the moat. Men labored in desperate haste, for the most deadly weapon of the infidel had not come into play. Perhaps a lucky shot from one of the mangonels had disarranged its apparatus. There was no telling.

Here it came at last with a horrible hiss and a fiery fuse at its tail, bursting on the edge of the bank and spreading liquid which broke at once into roaring flame, outlining the low shelters and revealing the twenty-foot depth of the moat with a small pile of earth at the bottom. Luckily the aim of a Greek-fire bomb was not any better than that of a mangonel, so that a good many burst harmlessly like the first. The shelters, moreover, were covered with loose hide which gave at impact and often allowed a bomb to roll off without being shattered. Nonetheless, the smoke was stifling, and in the absence of wind it hung in the tunnel up which the men had to stagger with their burdens. Godfrey was working his soldiers in relays and told some of the women, released from the toil of digging, to bring them drink.

On one stretch a mantlet hung burned out, so that the only protection was the wall of sacks which men had heaped inside it. On this part stones, fire, and arrows rained ceaselessly down, while a working party was trying to edge another screen into place.

A Greek-fire bomb fell squarely into the gap and broke on the path, drenching the workers in roaring, liquid flame. So frightful were their screams and so strong the smell of burning flesh that those coming up with earth shrank back appalled. Even when the flames burned out and the horrible sounds had died away, men hesitated, bunched together out of range, unwilling to plunge through the smoke and perhaps stumble over charred logs which had been men.

"Five nobles for the man who leads the way," cried Godfrey. The pale light of dawn was in the sky and the moat was halfway full. Things would go slower in broad daylight and with the work pushed close to the wall.

One of the waiting men threw down his sack. "Five nobles for a chance to burn! Not I."

"Five nobles for a cross to honor Saint Martin in our lord Godfrey's chapel!" Robert of Saint Avold had come down from the siege tower, where he had been waiting with the best of the knights to lead the way into the city. "Give me the sack!" he cried; and seizing it as lightly as though he were not weighted down with armor, he ran up to the moat and tossed it in.

"Get that screen forward!" Gilbert of Tournai, who had followed his friend, laid a hand on the mantlet and began to edge it forward. Men ran to help him, and the hole in the defense was covered. Others were following Robert through the smoke. One of Godfrey's mangonels with better aim than usual crashed into an infidel soldier exposing himself too insolently. A cheer arose from the ranks of the men-at-arms waiting with ladders to try and scale the wall when the attention of the besieged should be distracted by the tower.

"Wait till we get at them," screamed one. "We'll show them fire!"

The sun came up. Those who had toiled all night collapsed panting, covered with dust and bleeding from stones. Some of the women had raw and burning blisters on their hands. Even the clerics and holy men were helping with the digging, while the moat itself was filling with bodies and stones as well as earth.

The great siege tower lumbered into slow motion some time during the afternoon, pushed from behind by hundreds of people leaning on great bars built out for the purpose. It creaked and shuddered as it went, but yet it moved to the very lip of the moat, where it stuck because the passage was still uneven and stone-strewn. Men were working to smooth it, but the protection of the mangonels was not enough to prevent the defenders from heaving down vast rocks and liquid fire. Now the archers on the tower, some armed by this time with the eastern bow and all of them better armored than their opponents on the wall, swept the battlements clean. Protected by strong shelters, the enemy mangonels still played and the Greek-fire bomb emerged with sputter and hiss. These, however, fell haphazard, since nobody dared crane over the battlements to direct their aim.

"We have them, we have them!" Godfrey cried. He and his knights were jammed together in the second story of the tower, waiting to burst out over the bridge when it should be let down. The tower rocked on the lip of the moat and jolted forward.

There was almost a lull in the battle below. Some time earlier Godfrey had silenced his mangonels because they were doing more harm to the men in the moat than to those on the wall. As the tower came into close range, it drew all the fire of the enemy. Like the mantlets, it was covered with curtains of hide; and inside these it was made of heavy timber which shuddered and groaned under the bombardment. But the structure held, and on every story men were ready with sand to put out fire.

Three times the tower stuck in the moat while work crews labored frantically with pick and spade to smooth its path. There were great holes in its curtains now, and the archers on its battlemented roof had suffered severely.

With a final lurch it moved into place. With a yell of triumph men let its bridge crashing down, while far below men swarmed into the moat with ladders, starting to climb.

Gilbert of Tournai was first on the bridge with Robert behind him and Godfrey of Bouillon himself coming after that. Already the enemy was trying to hack its supports away, but since it was slung by great chains and heavy with the weight of armored men, they could not move it. For stones and Greek fire it was too late, now that the two sides were locked in hand-to-hand combat, the enemy assailing the foremost knights on the bridge, while those behind pushed forward. Robert was swept onward like a stone from one of the mangonels. He dashed his shield into one man's face and smashed at another with the mace which he preferred to a sword for hand-to-hand fighting. He laid about him furiously, towering above the battle, too busy to notice whether blood of friend or enemy spattered his armor.

The battle rose to its climax. Everyone was yelling. Those who were climbing the wall had the advantage that most of the defenders had been attracted towards the tower. Thus, though some ladders were dashed down and destroyed, their very numbers made it hard to prevent men gaining some sort of foothold. In front of the tower, a group of knights had pushed off the bridge and were fighting in the narrow walk behind the battlements, making for one of the turrets of the wall, from which they could descend into the town. Behind Godfrey's men, the forces of Tancred, Bohemond's nephew, were pressing up into the tower to cross the bridge.

They were off the wall and fighting in the streets. The armed defenders of the town were falling back, but men and women and even children hurled tiles from the rooftops. Refugees were caught in the narrow alleys. A girl with a baby in her arms was cut down by Hugo Grossetete. He snatched the child as she fell and dashed it to the cobbles. "Kill! Kill!" cried Gilbert of Tournai. Robert's arm was weary with hewing. He was dizzy with the excitement of conquest, drunk with blood.

In the better quarter of the town, many knights thought of plunder. Tancred's shield already hung over a door, as did Hugo Grossetete's. What was done within nobody knew, but the shrieks and screams of helpless people soon rose above the dying sounds of battle. Robert, who had thought it shame to desert the fray while men resisted, found opposition shredding away. He pursued it.

Panting, he came to a halt. There was nobody with him, and in front the last group of soldiers had vanished down an alley. He looked around, almost bewildered by the sudden silence, contrasting with the distant shouts and screams of the battle, now openly turning into a massacre. He put a hand up to his face and tried to mop it, impeded by the armored back of his glove and the nose-piece of his helmet.

It was nearly twenty-four hours since the battle had started. He had eaten and drunk during that time, but had not slept. The padding which he wore under his armor was soaked right through with sweat, and his mouth felt dry as leather.

Slowly he took in his surroundings. He was standing in a narrow, twisting street which suddenly ended in a wall and a great wooden door pierced by a grillwork through which the porter might peer at visitors. It reminded him of something which in the heat of the fight he had forgotten. He stood in Jerusalem, the end of his journey, and the feet of the Son of God had trodden these cobbles. Awestricken, he made the sign of the Cross. The grille in front of him looked familiar. What came to him was his own voice, saying to Theodore, "There was a door with a grille . . . and a court . . . we stabled our donkeys."

Robert walked up to the gate, put his hands on the grillwork, and with a mighty effort of strength, he tore it from the sockets in which it rested in the wood. He put his hand inside and felt for the bolt. The door swung open, revealing an outer courtyard in which, sure enough, lay manure from tethered donkeys. Robert unhitched his shield and slung it on the gate before he went in.

There was no one in the court, and the house still guarded its secrets by another blank wall and a closed door. But on the wall someone or other with hasty hand and dripping paint had traced a Cross. It was glittering and still wet.

Robert smiled grimly. So they thought the Cross would protect them, when all the army knew that the true Christians had been expelled from the city, lest they betray it.

Those who had remained were no better than infidels themselves. No, they were worse, seeing that they held the true faith but were faithful to those who denied it.

He strode up to the door and pushed; it opened with a creak, not even fastened. If the household was relying on the protection of the Cross, then they were lucky it was Robert of Saint Avold and not Hugo Grossetete whose shield hung on the gate. At least they would have a quick death.

This door had opened to reveal a garden surrounded by a colonnade and shaded by palm trees clustered about a marble pool. The place was almost a palace, considering that water must be as precious as silver in the city, dry at the best of times and now under siege!

Robert scanned the marble colonnades, wondering which led to the main apartments, where the servants were, what kind of merchant lived in a house like this and dared to be Christian. He did not have to wonder long, for in the shadow of the central colonnade he saw a woman.

She was tall and slender, dressed in a silk garment of a soft green that set off a brown complexion, cheeks slightly tinted with rouge, and black hair falling loosely about her shoulders. As she saw him, a mountain of a man in blood-stained armor, she gave a little gasp and lifted her right hand with a small dagger in it, turning the point towards her breast with an unmistakable threat to use it against herself if he came nearer.

Robert passed his tongue across his lips. His mouth was so dry that he could hardly speak, but after a minute he managed to croak in Arabic first, then Greek, "I must have

water!" Advancing to the pool, he took off his helmet and
filled it. It went down like nectar. He filled it again and
emptied it over his face and hair. Water ran down his neck,
and he gave a great sigh of relief. "Ah-ah!" he said.

The woman had stood perfectly quiet, her hand still raised
against herself while she stared at him out of eyes which had
been skilfully painted with blue shadows so that they looked
huge in her thin face. Now she said to him in clear Greek,
"We are Christian folk, but once my father did the Emir a
service. We have lived under his protection since, and so he
permitted us to stay throughout the siege."

"You had better have left," said Robert rather grimly, "instead of taking favors from the Moslem."

She met his gaze obstinately. "My father could not be
moved. I think he is dying."

Robert looked at her and then back to the house, wondering if its servants were inside or had fled altogether, leaving
their mistress to face what came. He remembered Theodore, the Moslem nobles he had met and secretly admired,
the native Christians, who had thought the infidel a better
master than their new Frankish lords. Slowly he nodded,
put down his mace by the pool, stripped off his gloves, and
walked towards her.

For a moment her lips parted in fright, but she seemed to
find reassurance in his broad red face and dripping hair, for
she let him come. He put out his huge hand and took the
dagger. It was a pretty, jeweled thing, but very sharp.

"Fear nothing," Robert said in his careful Greek. "You
are under my protection, and no one shall harm you." He

touched her fingers with the tip of his own. "There is my hand upon it."

The contact served as a greeting. Shyly they smiled at one another. For an instant Robert's memory flashed back to the grim little castle where his father had bidden him a long good-bye as he sent him to win fortune in the East. In retrospect, it looked small, gray, and cold. It was not probable that he would ever see it any more.

PART II

The Heir

1170

THE HOUSE of William the archdeacon lay within the walls of Tyre on a height of land near the cathedral, looking down over a huddle of roofs to the blue Mediterranean so that it caught the sea breezes without the smells which pervaded the harbor. It had originally been of modest size, but a new court recently added looked out through colonnades into the archbishop's garden, which that good man had put at the disposal of his colleague.

Archdeacon William, standing in a corner of the colonnade, smiled at the half-dozen boys in the garden who were

trying to see which one could walk the furthest on his hands.
William was a man of noble presence with a long, clever face
relieved from austerity by its expression. "So excellent a
prince!" he remarked quietly, making a gesture towards one
of the boys who was getting up, laughing. "God has been
good to give His kingdom such an heir!"

"You have fairly beaten me, Gerard," called the young
prince gaily, dusting himself off. "But I shall practice and
challenge you again!"

"Prince Baldwin always strives for excellence," murmured
the archdeacon.

Reynald, prince of Sidon, who had ridden in for the purpose of examining the archdeacon's manuscript collection,
looked faintly bored. A nine-year-old boy did not interest
him much, and he had a particular dislike for the prince's
mother, with whom his association had been brief and disas-
trous.

"King Amalric has chosen his tutor well," he remarked,
"for I see that Prince Baldwin means much to you already."

A twinkle in the archdeacon's eye betrayed his compre-
hension. "You are impatient, Prince Reynald, because you
have arrived at the wrong hour. Earlier in the afternoon I
would have been at your service, for the boys go to the tilt-
yard as soon as the breeze comes up. Of this I am quite free
and can only tell you that their instructor reports the prince
is perfectly fearless and will ride better than King Amalric."

"A paragon among princes!" said Reynald lightly. "God
save him from being spoiled by flattery."

William laughed. "After the riding, the boys are tired;

and it is their free hour. As they play in the garden, they know that I walk in the colonnade because I am not willing to let a servant supervise their leisure. But I do not interfere with what goes on, nor do they speak to me unless they wish to."

"And how long does this leisure endure?"

"Alas, till evensong. Can you curb your impatience until after our evening meal? The boys go early to bed, and I promise to sit up as long as you please."

Reynald smiled reluctantly. "Who would have thought the wise archdeacon would turn schoolmaster to a pack of boys!"

The boys had got tired of their game, and most of them were sitting on the coping of a small pool, trying to catch fish in their fingers and getting fairly damp in the process. Unobserved by his elders, one frail child with arms like matchsticks was still attempting to balance on his hands. Presently he fell in a huddle, hitting his head, and set up a wail.

"Crybaby!" exclaimed Gerard, reaching out to kick him.

"Ah, let Roger alone," protested Baldwin. "He's only seven."

Gerard flushed with annoyance. He was the tallest and strongest of the boys and liked to consider himself their leader. The prince's special position galled him, the more so because Baldwin constantly challenged him and occasionally beat him. Gerard got deliberately to his feet, walked over, and jerked Roger up by one arm. "Stop sniveling, or I'll give you something to cry about, you coward!"

Young Baldwin got up, too. "I said leave him alone!"

Deliberately Gerard lifted Roger's arm and took a pinch of it between thumb and forefinger. He twisted, cruelly digging his nails in; and Roger screamed.

Prince Baldwin took a flying leap and bore his enemy to the ground. They thrashed about, and Gerard tried to smash his opponent's head against the coping of the pond.

"Look out! You'll kill him," cried one of the other boys in alarm. He fell on the couple, and two more followed his example. They rolled in a milling mass across the gravel, while Roger wiped his eyes on the sleeve of his jerkin.

"Hm! So that's their play!" remarked the prince of Sidon. "Don't you ever stop such games when they get rough?"

"Not often," William said. "Indeed, I am grateful to Gerard because he does not give way to the prince when others do so."

The boys were sorting themselves out. Gerard had an ugly gash on his brown cheek which was trickling blood down his neck, but he ignored it. "They are all afraid of you," he scowled at Baldwin, "because when you are king they will owe you allegiance. When I grow up, I'm going to be Grand Master of the Knights Templars like my uncle. I shall owe allegiance to nobody but God and the Pope. You'll never be king over *me!*"

"All the same, you'll do as I say," young Baldwin retorted, squaring his shoulders. "Want to fight me about it?"

"Oh no you won't!" cried the boy who had first interfered. "Gerard doesn't fight fair when he loses his temper. He was trying to kill you."

"Too precious to be hurt!" said Gerard with a sneer.

Prince Baldwin looked around him, appearing to consider. His eye fell on little Roger sitting on the curb of the pool and rubbing his arm. "I'll tell you what," he said, "you pinch me the way you did Roger here, and I'll pinch you. The first one who flinches away or cries out is beaten. And to show you that I don't win because of my rank, I'll let you start." He rolled up his sleeve. "Arnulf can count to twenty while you do it. Slowly mind!"

Gerard grinned. "All right, my turn!" he seized the offered arm and took a generous pinch above the elbow.

"Start counting," Baldwin said easily as the fingers twisted. "Slowly."

William and the prince of Sidon watched over the oleander which in part at least concealed them from the boys. Baldwin stood perfectly easily, smiling at his opponent, who bent his dark head over the arm in a furious effort.

"Twenty!" called Arnulf. Gerard stripped his arm and held it out. The counting began again.

Gerard clenched his teeth and stood rigid, flushing deeply; but he made no sound. "That hurts," remarked the prince of Sidon. "He's a good boy."

"And the other? After all, he is only nine; and Gerard is eleven."

Reynald of Sidon nodded, impressed. The first duty of a king of Jerusalem was to defend his kingdom, often against odds. Endurance in battle was his best quality.

"In intelligence, too," the archdeacon told him, "Baldwin easily outstrips the others. See, he also has the manners of a prince!" Baldwin had released his opponent at the eighteenth count, protesting that Arnulf for his sake was counting slower.

He offered his arm for the second time, and Gerard made inspection to be sure that he took hold of the same spot. But dig and twist as he might, the prince neither changed color nor lost his easy smile. He might have been watching an operation on someone else's arm. Even the archdeacon was astonished. "All say that he has courage, but this is more than has been told to me."

For the second time it was Baldwin's turn. If Gerard had been red before, he was now white. He opened his mouth, but no sound came. "He'll not give in," said Reynald. "He'd die sooner."

"He's only a boy," said the archdeacon apologetically. "Listen!"

Slowly, breathlessly, through the open lips of the boy there came a sound, hardly above a whisper, of agony. "Ah-ah!"

Baldwin dropped his hand, and Gerard dashed the sleeve of his other arm across his eyes, where tears of rage and pain had started to gather. Abruptly he turned and rushed out of the court, passing close to where the prince and the archdeacon were standing.

"He doesn't like to say he lost," cried Arnulf angrily.

Baldwin shook his head. "Let him alone. He knows."

The little scene was at an end, and the prince sat down again, dabbling his hands in the pond with the air of one who was idling away his time in thoughtless fashion. The other boys gathered in a little knot to talk things over, steal-

ing occasional looks at the prince as they discussed him.
Some minutes passed before the tolling of the chapel bell
gave warning that it was time to make themselves tidy for
the evening service. Baldwin got up and led the way
through the colonnade. As he went past the two men, William called to him.

"Prince Baldwin, I have here with me Reynald, Prince of
Sidon, who is anxious to greet you."

Baldwin came readily, sufficiently accustomed to the manners of his father's court to give frank reverence, while yet
preserving an easy dignity. Seen closer, he was an attractive
youngster with a fine pair of gray-blue eyes and a sturdy
build. Reynald smiled at him. "You have courage, prince."

William added a graver commendation. "I shall praise
you to your father, and you know I will never do so unless
you have deserved it."

Quick color rushed into the boy's face, and for a moment
his princely poise deserted him entirely. He curled one leg
around the other and hung his head, not looking his master
in the eye.

"Why, what is the matter now?" inquired William gently.

"Perhaps you will think it was not chivalrous," muttered
the child, squirming. "But you told me, sir, that a man must
rule by his head, not always by force. So I thought — "
His voice trailed off.

"It was a good contest," Reynald told him, "and a better
test than fighting."

"Ah no!" the boy said quickly. "It wasn't really." He
turned back to William. "You see, I knew I would not feel

anything . . . If you think it was not chivalrous," he said in a rush, "I will admit to Gerard — "

"Baldwin," said William, frowning down on him from his great height, "whatever do you mean when you say you did not feel?"

"Oh, I never do in my arm," the child said easily. "Not up there anyway. So . . . was it fair?" He looked anxious.

William did not notice the question. "How long has your arm been numb like that?" His voice was sharp.

"Oh, I don't know. A long time." Suddenly William's tone appeared to register, for he added uneasily, "It's quite all right, sir, nothing wrong with it except peeling a little."

This time William made no answer at all, and the silence seemed endless, hardly interrupted by the boy repeating with an anxious note in his voice, "It *is* all right!" He flexed it hopefully. "It *is* all right!"

William opened his mouth, but no sound came. He swallowed and the prince of Sidon caught his breath audibly. "Why, of course it is all right," said William at last. "You must forgive me. I felt a rheumatic twinge in my bad shoulder." It must have been a painful twinge, for his face was gray. "So it peels a little, does it? In round patches? Perhaps you need a salve. Let me look at it."

He put out his hand to take the boy's arm, but Reynald stopped him. "Let the doctor have a look. It is his business. Don't *touch* it, William!"

William put his friend's hand aside. "We shall have Prince Baldwin thinking that there is something wrong when the only matter is that you do not trust my skill. To be sure the doctor shall give us a salve if it is needed, but we must not make much ado about little matters. The arm, as the prince says, is quite all right."

He took the arm gently and peeled back the sleeve, exposing a roughening in circular spots where the color of the skin was whiter than normal. He put out a finger and touched one of the spots, pressing on it. "Don't you feel that?"

The boy shook his head, regarding his master with frightened eyes. William let go the arm, holding his own hand a little away from his side as though for some reason he did not wish to use it for the present. "Well, run along and tidy yourself, lest you be late for evening prayers. I will send the chaplain to you this evening, for my shoulder pains me. Tomorrow perhaps the doctor had better give you a salve."

The boy ran off. William said nothing, but he raised his hand, palm up, and looked at his spread fingers while tears ran silently down either side of his big nose.

"Jesus, Maria, and all the Saints!" exclaimed Reynald in a horrified whisper. "And you touched him!"

"God forgive me!" said the archdeacon still looking at his hand, "for my flesh crawled."

"You are wrong," Reynald said in haste. "You must be wrong. You are no doctor, my friend. Some skin disease — "

"Oh, the doctors will see it, never fear; but I'm not wrong nor are you. The boy has leprosy, and I must tell his father."

"The King may have other sons. He is yet young."

"But not like this boy," William said. "So excellent a prince!" He let the tears trickle down his chin because he would not use his hand to wipe them away. "Ten years, fifteen at most, and you know how they die! The hand of God is heavy when a child must suffer so for the sins of the kingdom."

"Pray God for the kingdom," said Reynald softly, "and for the King." He was not more devoted to King Amalric than the archdeacon, nor even more of a statesman. But he cared less for the boy and thought of the need of the kingdom for a leader in battle, while William thought of Baldwin.

"The boy will have to know," said William, "and what then? This cannot be hidden even from him?"

"The King must have another son," repeated Reynald grimly. It was not easy to rear a healthy child in such a climate, and boys were harder to bring up than girls. But these were dangerous times, and the kingdom must have a leader.

William was not listening. "What a king he would have made, poor boy! What will he do now?"

The Possessors

1183

The road from Egypt ran north to Damascus through the red hills of Moab, skirting the kingdom of Jerusalem to the east of the Dead Sea. This was a much-traveled road, for Saladin had lately made himself sultan of both Egypt and Damascus, so that there was a great deal of commerce between them. In the hottest part of this day the road lay empty; for even after the first of the rains it was uncomfortable to travel. Nothing stirred except a poor old donkey abandoned by his master when he fell for the last time beneath his load. Around the dying animal a dozen vultures waited, each with a jealous eye on his own cousins and nest-mates, lest one of them try to get more than his share of the spoil. Now and then a bird would move inward impatiently; the others with suspicious calculation advanced for the same distance.

There is no hatred like that between heirs when a rich inheritance will shortly fall vacant. In the inner courtyard of the castle of Kerak, built on a precipitous ridge to dominate the road, stood its mistress, Stephanie of Milly, lady of Moab and all the parts of the kingdom beyond Jordan. Stiff with suspicion and pride, she waited under a canopy held over her head to spare her complexion, while the mother of her son's bride came forward to meet her.

Queen Maria Comnena, widow of the late King Amalric, and cousin to the Emperor himself, was aware that Stephanie, being of lower rank, must incline to her first. But the mistress of the castle had given offense by not advancing to greet her guests as they came across the drawbridge from the town. Queen Maria held her head high as she surveyed her rival.

Neither lady could claim to outshine the other in costume, for the visitors had changed their clothes in tents set up for the purpose before they made their entry into the town. Queen Maria blazed in cloth of gold worn over scarlet, while Stephanie was dressed in embroidered blue and cloth of silver. In height Stephanie had the advantage, for the queen was short and a trifle squat of figure. But the lady of Milly by now was nearly forty and a blonde in a climate which was not kind to fair complexions. Queen Maria's dark eyes were still lustrous, her lips so delicately colored that they passed for natural, her smooth skin a rich brown.

"That dreadful nose of hers!" thought Stephanie. "She'll certainly burst out of that dress if she grows any fatter." Coolly she sketched an inclination and a curtsey.

"Her teeth are growing yellow, and she plasters on paint to hide her bad complexion." Queen Maria responded with what was hardly more than a nod, slightly parting her lips to show her own white teeth.

The sun blazed down upon a brilliant scene. The castle of Kerak had outfitted its men-at-arms in new russet jerkins, while its bachelor knights were flaunting eastern turbans and plunder from the caravans of the great road. Over the flagstones upon which Stephanie had taken her stand lay a priceless carpet of eastern work, its blues and pinks blending with the colors of her gown. The castle trumpeters performed a final flourish of welcome and fell silent, while the ladies waited for each other to begin speaking.

A moment of awkwardness followed which was broken by Reynald of Chatillon, the lady of Milly's present husband. There was something indestructible about Reynald, a jovial, coarse, back-slapping man who had miraculously managed to survive for sixty years while better men, or so some said, succumbed to war and diseases of the climate.

"Where is the bride?" roared Reynald, bustling forward. "Why, Humphrey, boy, this is no time to dally when you bring me a stepdaughter home to Kerak. Time later for your kisses, eh? First, by the bones of God, I'll kiss her myself!"

Humphrey, the seventeen-year-old lord of Toron and heir to the vast domains of the lady of Milly, came forward leading the princess Isabella, stepsister of King Baldwin. They made a pretty pair. Humphrey of Toron had long fair hair and was blushing like a girl; while his little princess, hardly out of childhood, was clad in a soft pink gown, sewn with pearls and bordered with silver. A veil, fine as a spiderweb, covered her hair beneath a coronet, also of pearls.

Isabella had been taught that she must kneel to her new mother, but Reynald had not been included in her instructions. She shrank towards her bridegroom, glancing at him with a soft look of appeal. While the boy hesitated, Reynald took her in his arms and kissed her heavily on the mouth. It was plain to everyone that she struggled and tried to push him away, but Reynald only gave his roaring laugh as he released her and saw she was in tears. "Shy, daughter, eh? It's too late to be shy. You can tell your bridegroom that Reynald of Chatillon taught you how to kiss."

Balian of Ibelin, Queen Maria's present husband, murmured to his brother, "Watch out for the wolf when he plays the buffoon."

"Watch out for the lambs," retorted Baldwin of Ibelin, eyes on the young couple as they went on their knees before Stephanie. He shook his head gloomily. "Young Humphrey looks too gentle to become a king. But Toron is a name which may unite faction."

After their welcome, wine was offered to refresh the travelers. Scented water was carried in silver ewers to turret rooms cooled by the thickness of the wall. Here the guests took their siestas on cushions of down and coverlets of silk. On tables inlaid with ivory or silver stood bowls of figs and apples, together with crystal goblets filled with a drink made out of pomegranate juice.

"Reynald of Chatillon lives like a king," remarked Hugo of Saint Avold, who had come out on pilgrimage from France and was at present riding with his eastern cousin Rainier in the train of the Ibelins. "Why even the King of France has not silken hangings or silver lamps such as these."

"In the kingdom of Jerusalem," said his cousin Rainier grimly, "a great lord's life is short. He enjoys what he can."

Hugo inspected the carpet with a dubious air. One could spit into rushes at Saint Avold, and they took no harm. It was a great piece of ill-fortune that he should have arrived in a time of truce and would not have the honor of riding against the infidel. For all their warlike talk, these lords had gone soft with good living and preferred a truce to their plain Christian duty. He opened his mouth to grumble. "If King Baldwin would only — " Then he remembered about King Baldwin and fell silent.

"The King can no longer move without help," Rainier told him bluntly. "His hands and feet are rotting, and people say that spices must be burned in his room night and day to overcome the smell of corruption."

"Just like these spices here," said Hugo, jerking a contemptuous thumb towards a bowl standing ready beside the fireplace, which was laid with logs lest the turret room be damp or cold during the rains. Privately he thought that

Kerak, and indeed the whole kingdom of Jerusalem, smelled rotten.

No doubt the King of France lacked lamps or hangings like those of Kerak. Certainly he did not have such cooks, such costly flavors, so many meats, such trifles of spun sugar, such cakes of almond paste or sweet mulled wine. Queen Maria, who liked her food, began to mellow at the banquet; while Stephanie sent the musicians a dish from her own table because Balian of Ibelin, who was sitting next her, praised them.

Reynald was growing red in the face. He was wearing a ruby as big as a pigeon's egg in the front of his turban. "I took it," he boasted to Queen Maria, "out of the pack of one of those merchants we raided last year. It was meant for Saladin."

His booming voice went down the table and produced silence. "Is it true," asked Balian of Ibelin softly, "that when you broke the truce and would not give up your spoil, even at King Baldwin's command, Saladin made a vow — "

"That he would cut off my head with his own hand!" Reynald laughed and stroked his neck. "It is still on my shoulders. A short life and a merry one, says the proverb; but for my part I say that those who are merriest live longest." He drained his cup and set it down to be refilled. He stood up waving it. "I'll give you a loyal toast. Long life to King Baldwin!"

Balian of Ibelin jumped up. "Sit down, for shame!"

Reynald would not be silenced. "The King can no longer ride to war, so he makes a truce with Saladin. Fat little mice

start running past a rock where a great cat sits waiting in
Kerak. Sooner or later I pounce. No one restrains me because King Baldwin rots and Saladin is busy with plots or
rumors of plots against his person. Therefore good luck to
the plotters, say I, and long live King Baldwin the Leper."

"By the beard of the Prophet," cried Balian, swearing in
Arabic, "dare you boast of brigandage which has endan-
gered the whole kingdom?"

"I swear my oaths by the bones of God like a good Christian," answered Reynald insultingly. "And I make myself
feared by the infidel. You Ibelins have no idea what's needed
on a frontier."

Hugo of Saint Avold nodded approvingly. Here at least
was a man such as they understood in France.

"Sit down, Balian," said Baldwin sharply to his brother.
"Will you spoil our wedding feast by squabbling over what
is done and cannot be undone?"

"Saladin might break the truce tonight and none could
blame him," said Balian sullenly; but he sat down.

The lady Stephanie, who also thought that things had
gone too far, came to the rescue. She beckoned to her steward. "What entertainments have you tonight?" She turned
to the company. "You must know that for days all the jugglers and dancers that are to be found in the East have been
crowding into Kerak, so that Simon here has had hard work
to discover which will give the finest show. Let us wait his
decision."

Simon hesitated, turning away from the meat he was carv-
ing. "If you please, my lady —"

"What's the matter?"

He spread his hands in a helpless gesture. "My lady . . . they all went away!"

"They went?" Stephanie stared at the steward blankly. "You mean the entertainers who came for the wedding? They went where?"

"The gates of the town were open, my lady; and they vanished."

"They heard something!" Reynald's voice was suddenly sharp. "Who brought a message?"

"There was coming and going all day long," answered Simon weakly.

This was unquestionably true. A short silence followed, broken by Balian saying that since they must entertain themselves, his squire Rainier had brought a mandolin and knew the latest love songs to please the ladies. This found favor with Stephanie, so that presently the banquet once more took on the appearance of a joyous celebration. But under cover of the music, Reynald beckoned to a hard-faced knight who was his seneschal and muttered in his ear. The man went away and did not return. From the lower tables a few of Reynald's bachelor knights began to drift out.

"What's the matter?" asked Hugo of Saint Avold of one of these.

"Time to post the sentries, raise the drawbridge, and see that the gates are closed around the town. Just evening routine." The knight disappeared. Stephanie of Milly followed his movements with her eyes. Her color was too high as she smiled on Balian, congratulating him on the talent of his squire.

"Though if he were not the bridegroom, my Humphrey could show you that we are not without singers here in Kerak."

Balian smiled in agreement, watching the bridegroom crumble his bread and bite his lip as he glanced uneasily at the door through which another of Reynald's younger fighting men was going out. Balian told Stephanie that her son had the reputation of being as gifted for love as for war and that it was pretty to see the delight of the princess in her bridegroom.

With empty compliments and false smiles the banquet proceeded, while sentries mounted the castle walls and sharp commands were given that the sheep grazing the ridge be driven inside the town. Reynald was well aware no light threat would have driven the entertainers away before so rich a wedding. Careful questions were asked of the townsfolk who were Arabic-speaking, but no one knew what had been whispered around. Besides, so many had gone out to visit the tents set up for the Ibelins that even the gatemen had not noticed how few had returned.

That night the sentries of Kerak peered over moonlit walls that rose so steeply from the precipitous rock that only on the north through the town could the castle be approached. Not even the Bedouin stirred in those deep valleys, and nothing was heard on the narrow ridge but a distant jackal. On the top of a tower on the western side

Reynald's men kept logs for a beacon to flash a warning which, picked up by relays, would be known in Jerusalem in a couple of hours. These lay undisturbed as night wore on and guards were changed. "All's well!" chanted the watchman, making his hourly rounds in the little town.

In the morning of the following day the chapel of Kerak was lighted for the wedding by wax candles in great iron chandeliers swinging low. There were other candles before the piece of Our Lady's veil on the altar in a golden reliquary. They lit up the casket containing the bones of Saint Simeon brightly enameled with pictures of the Saint's life. Branches of candles on the walls flickered over pictures of Our Lady and the Saints, who seemed to move. Even the fruit and flowers carved on the heads of the columns stirred visibly as the little flames below them flared or dimmed.

Young Humphrey was clad in white satin embroidered with gold and bordered with ermine. His tiny princess wore a trailing robe of white brocade which fell away on either side revealing an underdress shot with pink and green and purple like the plumage of a dove. The bishop brought to unite them was an old, frail man whose hands were seen to tremble as he joined those of the bride and groom together. This was a strange wedding for a princess, unattended by the King himself or by the King's full sister and her worthless husband whom the barons hated.

The bishop's quavering Latin was drowned by the call of a trumpet taken up by others on the walls around the castle. Distant shouts arose. A man-at-arms came running up the aisle to meet with Reynald halfway down it. They swept out

of the great door together, Reynald's knights hurrying behind them. It slammed shut.

The knights and squires in the train of the Ibelins were
crowding into the aisle. "Saladin!" exclaimed Hugo of Saint
Avold, who had been nearest the door. His voice was exult-
ant. "The infidel is up in force from Egypt. It is Saladin's
army, and the truce is over!"

"Go on, go on!" shouted Baldwin of Ibelin to the bishop.
"We are come here for a wedding, and we shall not stir until
it is completed."

His voice quelled the disturbance in the chapel, but not
the uproar outside. Humphrey of Toron had dropped Isabella's hand to fumble uncertainly with the small jeweled
dagger he wore for ornament. His back was to his bride.
The mouth of the bishop hung open, but as far as anyone
could hear, no voice came out of it.

"Lord of Toron," cried Baldwin with angry contempt,
"are you so girlish that a mere alarm destroys your wits?
Then let a better man have the bride and with her the kingdom!"

The boy flushed red as he turned back to Isabella, reaching for her hand. The chaplain of Kerak, assisting the
bishop, leaned forward to prompt him. In a frightened murmur the old man took up the marriage service, starting in
the middle of a sentence at the very word where he had
broken off. The knights of the Ibelins moved back into
their places. Stephanie and Queen Maria, each too great a
lady to show discomposure, darted angry glances at their
ladies to quell whispers.

Saladin was up from Egypt indeed. He had moved by forced marches, gathering the Bedouin into his net, lest they warn Reynald. Early that morning his forces, moving round the hills in a great circle, had reached the northern end of the narrow ridge which led to the town. At the very moment they were sighted, his men swept into a charge, foot soldiers running behind the cavalry with scaling ladders.

The walls of the town were not high because their circumference was too great to permit of their being properly defended. Stores of food for times of siege were kept in the castle, as were great cisterns filled by the rains with storage water. In fact, the walls of the town were merely intended to delay attack while the defenders crowded across the drawbridge, taking their animals with them.

It was the sheep that Reynald chiefly needed, but the flocks were easily panicked in the confusion of narrow streets through which Reynald and his knights were hurrying to direct the defenders. Besides, when day had dawned uneventfully, the seneschal had given permission for the town gates to be opened so that animals might be grazed on the hillside. He was reluctant to use the hay which had been stored for fodder.

For such reasons, when the men of Saladin swept yelling across the ridge, the town gates were jammed open by a press of men and animals desperate to get inside. Similarly, many of Reynald's men were pinned on the drawbridge as they tried to rush out of the castle through the crowd.

There was desperate fighting at the gates which drew the town garrison from the walls. By the time these could be closed, the ladders planted elsewhere had found unguarded spots. Groups of infidels were already fighting for control of the towers through which they could descend into the town.

Presently the shouts and screams and the clashing of swordplay warned Reynald, busy directing the defense of the gates, that he must fall back. A band of infidels had cut its way through the town to the head of the drawbridge, scattering the rustics who were still trying to get into the castle.

"Wind up the bridge!"

The guards hesitated, knowing well that their commander and most of his men were cut off in the town.

"Wind up the bridge, I say!"

"No, leave it down!" Hugo of Saint Avold had stolen a march on the Ibelins by sending a page out of the church to fetch the armor, which he had brought with him to ride in a tournament. Thus when the wedding party emerged in unseemly haste, Hugo had stripped his outer clothes in the courtyard and buckled on his mail. As big a man as his great-uncle who had ridden in the train of Godfrey of Bouillon, Hugo advanced to the end of the drawbridge, where in the narrow space only one at a time could attack him.

The enemy did not come on. Indeed, they slightly recoiled from the bridge's end, clearly frightened of opposing their slighter strength and looser garments to the huge figure in clanking body-armor. Several of them had bows, and stones were also handy. Hugo received what missiles he could on his shield, which presently bristled with arrows. Stones rebounded from his helmet, arm, or legs, making to all appearances no more impression than they would have done on the castle wall.

"Come on!" he roared, brandishing his sword. An arrow hit him on the back of the mailed glove and penetrated, causing him to drop his weapon. With a high shout, the nearest of the Saracens was on him. Hugo dodged a spear and with a great bound forward dashed the edge of his shield so hard against his opponent that he fell in his tracks. A well-aimed arrow from the castle wall transfixed the man behind him, so that Hugo had time to stoop and pick up his sword, which he clasped in a dripping hand.

"Come on!" he challenged again; but by now the castle bowmen had cleared a space across which none dared leap. Behind the Saracens, Reynald's men burst yelling out of the town. The crisis was over. Reynald rode in laughing with an arm round Hugo's shoulders, while behind him the screams of women and children rose on the air.

Reynald was in high spirits. The loss of the town only meant that there would be fewer noncombatants to feed. He grinned at Balian, who was gloomily surveying the court-yard, now full of sheep, crying children, shouting men, and women sitting patiently on bundles. "Alas, I see there is no room for tilting; but we can offer you brisk action instead. You need not fear being bored, Lord Balian."

Balian was saved the need to reply by a whirr and a clank, followed by a distant crash, which proclaimed that the castle was firing off its mangonels. Reynald shrugged. "They'll be bringing up machines if I know Saladin, but the stone has yet to be quarried which will make an impression on Kerak."

"Has it ever stood a formal siege?" asked Balian rudely.

The lady Stephanie picked her way across the courtyard with two of her maids in attendance. "Now is this not too bad?" she called to Balian. "It is ungallant of Saladin to interrupt our wedding."

"No doubt he will call his people off," replied Balian with icy politeness.

Stephanie smiled coyly. "When I was a little maiden — oh, many years ago," she gestured with her hand to indicate how little a maiden she had been, "this Saladin was young and unimportant. My father accepted him as a hostage for the payment of some ransom, and he wrote a poem to me then. No doubt he had never seen yellow hair before . . . but it was a long time ago."

"Once seen, the lady of Milly is not lightly forgotten," rejoined Balian without enthusiasm. He was wishing that he could slip away to consult with his brother.

Stephanie clapped her hands. "I shall send Saladin some meats from our wedding table! I will dress them with my own hand. He will not have forgotten!"

Even Reynald was not paying her attention. He was scanning the confusion in the courtyard. "When our stores are better arranged, we may put up lists for swordplay. Or I have a leopard which we may bait with dogs. We'll not want for amusement."

Balian turned on his heel and walked away. The brigand

of Kerak had deliberately broken the truce and yet had neglected to post scouts, relying, forsooth, on the Bedouin for information. As a result, half the barons of the kingdom were bottled up in his castle, not to mention the newly married pair who were to have succeeded King Baldwin. Not that there would be a kingdom left if they all met disaster! Balian was too angry for jesting with Reynald, and yet he knew he was in the man's power and must control his feelings.

The wedding feast that night was more magnificent than ever. Indeed, it was a shocking waste of food, depriving everyone of appetite by its sheer extravagance. The enemy's mangonels were already playing on the outer wall, so that the dull thudding of stones served as a reminder that castle stores were not inexhaustible.

"Reynald says the siege will soon be raised," whispered Hugo of Saint Avold, in whom Reynald had found a kindred spirit. "Jerusalem cannot afford the loss of Kerak."

Rainier bit his lip. For at least the hundredth time he was out of sympathy with his kinsman, who had come bumbling over from France full of notions which were as out-of-date as his great-uncle. The kingdom lay like a ripe nut in the jaws of Saladin, twin jaws which were Egypt and Damascus. As long as King Baldwin could fight, he had kept the jaws open, leading his men in battle until he could no longer sit a horse. But now no one obeyed a king who could not move, was almost blind, who spoke in a mumble from behind curtains and stank of corruption. His sister Sibylla and her worthless husband would not stir to rescue a married pair who were their rivals for the throne. Sibylla and Guy were too foolish to care if by losing Kerak they laid open the flank of the whole kingdom.

A procession was coming into the hall from the kitchen, displaying the viands which the lady of Milly was sending to Saladin. With her own hands she had dressed a fine roast, which lay encircled by a gilded crown bearing the arms of Toron. For his part, the chief cook had made a pasty in the shape of the castle of Kerak, gay with flags and little figures carved of wood and brightly painted. Sweetmeats followed shaped in the likeness of a clutch of eggs in a gilded nest presided over by a pair of turtledoves. Other confections baked into hearts or true-lovers' knots were piled in horns of plenty decked with ribbons. At the rear of the procession came a dish on which, wreathed in laurel, lay a portrait of Stephanie with her golden hair about her shoulders.

Queen Maria might sniff with disdain, but the barons shouted their applause, for the gesture had spirit. Trumpets sounded for a parley. While the drawbridge creaked down, hard-faced men stood over the gateway, peering through slits with Greek fire lying handy in case of treachery. Judging others by what he was himself, Reynald trusted no one.

In a little over an hour the messengers returned laden with rare wines and ripe fruits for the wedding feast. To Stephanie Saladin sent a great blue stone and a fine scroll on which there was written a quatrain of the Persian poet Omar. Humphrey of Toron translated it to the company, for he was a scholar of some note and a lover of Omar.

"This is playacting, not war," thought Hugo of Saint Avold.

To the bride and groom Saladin sent twin goblets of crystal and a message. If the castle would fly a standard on the turret in which they slept, he would spare it the shots of his mangonels. He wished them pleasant dreams.

Reynald slapped his side and burst into loud laughter. "By the bones of God, you shall sleep in the turret west of the gate." This was the position of easiest approach, so that at the moment Saladin had four of his seven machines focussed upon it.

Saladin was as good as his word, but when the frightened children were put into their marriage bed with music and laughter, engines were still playing on the other side of the gate, so that the crash of stones came heavily through the slitted windows. They lay with their arms about each other, and the princess shuddered as she listened.

"I do not really want to be queen," she whispered to her bridegroom.

"Nor do I want to be king," confessed Humphrey of Toron.

Next morning Reynald put up lists in the great courtyard, and there was swordplay in which Hugo of Saint Avold won a chaplet presented by the bride's hand. The following day there were displays of wrestling, and the leopard was baited. The ladies shrieked as the dogs were mauled, or the men betted. Every evening there was dancing. The castle of Kerak exhausted itself in celebrations, ignoring the red eyes

of the princess, the snappishness of Queen Maria, and the
dark looks of the Ibelins. Gradually nerves grew taut, beyond bearing. The lady of Milly boxed the ears of her new
daughter-in-law and forbade her to receive her mother in
her private apartments.

"I know what she says behind my back, and I'll not endure
it. It is time you learned to take your husband's side."

Queen Maria went raging to Balian. Her only daughter
was turning a traitor after four days of marriage! Balian
promised to speak to Reynald, but prudence overcame his
resolution. He merely asked if beacon signals had been seen,
promising succor.

Reynald was quite unconcerned. As he pointed out, a
beacon would serve to warn Saladin as well as to reassure the
castle. An army would come because it had to come. In any
case, his good friend, the Master of the Templars, would see
to it.

Balian received this opinion with gloom. He did not like
the Grand Master, and in his opinion the Knights Templar
were famous for ruthlessness rather than generalship. Besides, the seneschal of the kingdom was the brother of that
stupid Guy who had married the princess Sibylla. Balian
was desperately anxious, and yet he was angry that the brig-
and who had got them into this fix should be in a position
to demand an army at will from the whole kingdom.

That evening in the banqueting hall the tables groaned
with viands, yet Balian thought he saw signs of diminishing
plenty.

"The Wolf grows anxious, I think," he whispered to his brother. "Even Reynald is aware that the barons lack a leader who can summon them to war."

Baldwin dipped his fingers in a silver basin and dried them on a napkin offered by a page on bended knee. "No one but King Baldwin truly cares for the kingdom. If he had not been a leper, what a king he would have made!"

Days went by. The bishop went the round of the battlements with Our Lady's veil in its golden casket, while the bones of Saint Simeon were carried before him. The lookout post on the western tower was manned by night and day. The barons grew bored and laid bets on a duel that the castle mangonels were fighting with enemy machines. There was talk of a sortie, but nothing came of it. Hugo of Saint Avold was disgusted, but his cousin pointed out that Saladin's army could better afford losses than could the garrison. "Time enough for a sortie when help is sighted," said he.

No signal came, but the lookout men reported that there was a cloud of dust low down on the western horizon which could mean an army on the march. Everybody crowded up to the tower to have a look and down to the court again to burnish weapons or borrow from the castle store. For the first time the bustle in the castle seemed to have a purpose. However, later in the day the dust disappeared. Balian went to visit the tower to the east of the gate which was being still pounded by the mangonels. He reported to his brother that Reynald was having it shored up from within, certain sign that the bombardment was taking effect. The two brothers were not particularly alike, save that they were short, dark men, but their expressions of gloom had increased their resemblance. Neither believed in the relieving army . . . and if by a miracle one had come together, it would lack a general. Appalling disaster might result from insufficient forces making a rash attack on Saladin.

That night the twinkle of campfires was plainly visible a long day's march away, and the castle banquet took on an air of excitement, though the Ibelins still sat in silence. By this time there was no mingling of the two factions. Queen Maria's ladies would not speak to those of Stephanie, while knights and barons were clustered in unfriendly groups, each eyeing the other with ill-concealed resentment. Hugo of Saint Avold, who had quite gone over into Reynald's faction, avoided his cousin. The alliance which was to have been cemented by the marriage was crumbling faster than the castle wall, and no one was exerting himself to repair the breach. Reynald of Chatillon was offensive in his triumph, boasting of having brought the whole kingdom to heel. He drank a toast to "King Humphrey," openly implying that the kingdom would shortly be ruled from the castle of Kerak. This was too much for Balian.

"Best wait and see whether your friends arrive," he said sourly. "Saladin may have a reckoning with them first."

Reynald snapped his fingers. "That for Saladin! He'll slink away like the fox to his lair. He'll break up the siege and be off." He grinned at Balian. "I'll tell you something! My ears are better than yours. The mangonels have stopped."

There was utter silence in the hall as everyone listened.

The crash of the mangonels, muted at this distance to a dull thudding, had been so constant that by this time it was ignored. Indeed, when people failed to hear, they imagined that their own ears had ceased to register. Only after a long minute did cheering break forth.

"A sortie, a sortie!" cried Hugo of Saint Avold.

The shout was taken up, and there was a rush for armor, Reynald himself leading the way. Balian caught up with him in the courtyard.

"Are you mad?" he cried indignantly. "Saladin will be on his guard against this very thing. Besides, what need of it if we are to be rescued?"

Reynald shook him off. "Stay at home and look after the women! Do you think Saladin may come up against Kerak and slink away unscathed? That is not the fashion of Kerak, nor yet of Prince Reynald. We'll give Saladin his chance to take off my head!" He snatched his helmet from a squire and called for his charger.

"Fool!" muttered Balian, turning away. He looked glumly round the courtyard, where it was evident that the resentments of the siege were finding release. Even the barons who followed the Ibelins were eager to discharge pent-up feelings by hitting someone with whom they could properly quarrel. Already they were clustering around the gigantic form of Hugo of Saint Avold.

Balian knew when he was beaten. It was obvious that pride would prevent his knights from holding back, even at his order. Angrily he found his way to the gatehouse where he found his brother Baldwin superintending arrangements to let the drawbridge down. Since the fools would have their sortie, Baldwin said, someone had better make sure the castle was not captured in their absence. In Islam fools did not rise to power or brigands prosper.

As the drawbridge thudded down, the knights, disdaining concealment, swept forward with a yell. Their war cries were immediately matched by infidel shouts, and arrows whistled from the shelters put up for the mangonels. The moonlight was clear enough for shooting, while the rubble-strewn space beyond the moat held up the horses. For a moment the knights were thrown into confusion, but Hugo of Saint Avold rallied them with a war cry which resounded over the other shouts and the clashing of armor. They charged across the open space and disappeared into the huddle of mean buildings which comprised most of the town.

Balian and Baldwin had collected a company of archers and men-at-arms to hold the bridge, for the enemy was trying to pour Greek fire upon it, so that a second sally was needed to drive them back and smash their machines. Presently these were burning briskly, casting a lurid glow on a scene of great confusion. Infidels swarmed out of the dark like wasps, and the men-at-arms retreated with all convenient haste to the shelter of the drawbridge, leaving a score of corpses on the ground. A violent battle, to judge from the noise, was going on in the darkness between the knights and the main body of Saladin's army. From the drawbridge it was impossible to make any judgment on how that struggle went, save that the Saracens had been ready for it.

Fresh streams of infidels rushed at the drawbridge with

grappling irons to keep it down. But the battlements of the gatehouse had catapults on them which let fly volleys of stones, while archers stationed at the slits in the two towers of the gate rained arrows. Balian had the drawbridge raised about five feet, so that it was not easy for the infidel to force their way onto it, while yet it could be lowered in haste if need arose.

The battle in the streets was growing louder, sure sign that the knights were in retreat. Balian peered anxiously at the dark, calculating the right moment to let down the bridge and lead a charge to clear the foot of it. Fearful of being too late, he gave the word too early, only to find himself battling in desperation against foes whose numbers appeared to grow with every second. Nor dared Baldwin, directing the defense of the castle, allow his archers to shoot into the mass.

For a few minutes everything swayed in the balance. People were stabbing and being stabbed by figures only half-seen in the dark. Saracens pushed towards the drawbridge in such numbers that some lost their footing and fell with a scream into the thirty-foot dry-ditch which took the place of a moat until such time as the rains filled it.

Balian laid about him with his sword. He was hoarse with shouting, but the enemy were shredding away. The knights were coming back, mingling with the men-at-arms in a confused mass which streamed across the bridge into the castle, carrying with it not only Balian, but a dozen Saracens too close in the press to be able to get out. Other Saracens followed at the garrison's heels, keeping the drawbridge down by sheer weight. Baldwin dropped the portcullis with a crash in their very faces. From the gateroom over the arch his men poured down Greek fire, while the archers from the twin turrets rained arrows on them. With horrible cries the mass dissolved and fled. The drawbridge creaked up, and the last Saracen was cut down in the courtyard. In the light of torches, the garrison took stock and counted losses.

These were considerable. Hugo of Saint Avold had gone down in the press with Rainier, his cousin, a dozen or so of Reynald's knights, and several of the barons. Many of the rest were wounded, and the men-at-arms had suffered severely. Balian himself had a cut on his sword arm which he had not noticed until the great portcullis clanged behind him.

Reynald, who had come through without a scratch, was unrepentant about having led a sortie resulting in the loss of so many men. He grinned at Balian, remarking that he had promised the party should not be bored. "Nothing like a little brush with the enemy for excitement."

"It is understood that you care nothing," snapped Balian, too angry to be discreet, "about the fate of my friends; but what about yours? Or have you no friends at all, even in Kerak?"

"Pho!" Reynald shrugged it off. "Most of them aren't dead, and Saladin will hold noble prisoners to ransom. Mark my words, he will draw off now that we have shown him our teeth. He'll not stay here to be caught between us and the army coming to our rescue. Make the infidel fear you, man! It's the only way to deal with them."

Balian choked in his rage, for one of those missing was his own seneschal and close connection. But Baldwin took him by the arm as if to remind him that there was no arguing with such as Reynald. Next morning Saladin was seen indeed to be moving; and Reynald loudly claimed the credit, though Balian muttered that the mangonels had ceased before the sortie. One of the foot soldiers returned to the castle under flag of truce and brought the names of noble prisoners, including Rainier and Balian's seneschal. Hugo of Saint Avold was discovered by scouts that afternoon, dead and stripped of his armor. The old bishop said that he was in Heaven; but Balian whispered to his brother that one could go to Heaven at any time, but that meanwhile Hugo's father had lost an only son and the kingdom a knight who could be ill spared.

By the late afternoon, Saladin was in full retreat, and the Christian army was coming into view along the ridge. The drawbridge of the castle was let down, while its defenders with Reynald at their head streamed out to greet their friends. They met them in the little level space outside the town where the tents of the Ibelins had been pitched before the wedding.

"Did I not say so?" boasted Reynald in triumph, as he counted the pennons with an experienced eye. "Not only the Templars, but the Knights of Saint John, not only the barons, but the seneschal himself! They did not dare to risk the loss of Kerak."

"They have the True Cross with them," agreed Balian. He blinked incredulously. "And the royal standard. . . .

Can it be that King Baldwin is dead?" His voice was worried. If Guy of Lusignan had made himself king already, Isabella and her Humphrey, Queen Maria, and the Ibelins in general stood in danger. Would the barons and the Knights of the Orders sink their jealousies to serve under that upstart? He could hardly believe it.

"Guy of Lusignan's banner waves on the left," said Baldwin quietly. "They have brought the royal standard because the army came out in the King's name."

Balian sighed with relief. It must indeed be so! God wrought miraculous cures, but not for leprosy. The royal standard was brought at the barons' wish, since even to save Kerak, they grudged the seneschal full authority. Amalric of Lusignan was abler than his brother Guy, but loved by no one. "All is not yet lost for your son and my daughter," he said to Reynald, hoping their alliance might present some sort of united front, no matter how it galled him to have to depend on such a man.

Reynald made him no answer, not being certain on what side his interest lay. He was half of the opinion that alliance with the Ibelins would not prosper. He might use it to get a great price from the opposite side. At least he might angle for offers.

"Let us wait to greet them here," he said and reined up his horse.

The party from Kerak made a fine show, for the barons had dressed themselves in all the splendor they had brought for the tournament. Their banners were of silk, their lance-shafts gilded, the harness of their horses glittering with gold.

The oncoming army had halted on the hillside, apparently preparing to encamp there for the night, but a group of their leaders rode forward, among whom were the Grand Masters of the Knightly Orders, conspicuous by the great red or white cross which covered their surcoats.

Reynald greeted them with thanks. He could be courteous when he chose, for many years ago he had been husband to the reigning princess of Antioch, from whose family the Emperor himself had deigned to choose a wife. In his manner to the seneschal there was no hint of the reluctance with which Amalric must have come to rescue the Ibelin party. Indeed so fulsome was his welcome that Balian glowered and Reynald of Sidon, sitting a black horse beside the Master of the Knights of Saint John, said abruptly:

"Your thanks are due the King, for no authority but his would have brought the barons out to rescue Kerak."

"My thanks are surely due to the King," said Reynald, stiffening, for he did not like the prince of Sidon any better than he did the Ibelins. "And you may bear them to him, since my position in Kerak is too exposed for me to leave the castle." Privately he was glad to be spared the humiliation of thanking the King, whose commands he had set at defiance in that old matter of breaking the truce. He grinned at the prince of Sidon, taunting him with being a messenger and go-between.

"You may take them to him yourself," said the prince of Sidon, showing anger. "There flies his standard."

Reynald was so astonished that he dropped the reins on his horse's neck and stared. There was a dead silence.

"Then who . . . is the King?" he said at last.

"King Baldwin the Fourth, son of King Amalric," said the prince of Sidon proudly. "Whom else would the barons follow?" He turned his back on the seneschal and pointed. "Here comes his litter."

The royal standard was indeed advancing, followed by a clumsy curtained bed, slung between two horses and lurching cruelly over the uneven ground. Reynald stared at it, his normally high complexion mottled between red and gray, while a convulsive clutch at the reins moved his horse uneasily backward. "The Leper King!" he said in a whisper, shedding for the first time since Balian had known him courtly manners and brigand truculence alike. It was obvious that here at last was one thing Reynald feared.

Balian looked at him with loathing. The King was hideously dying, and he had taken his agony to war to shame the barons into the rescue of a man who had defied him. This martyrdom he had endured for the sake of the kingdom.

"By the beard of the prophet," he swore, "here is indeed a king to outmatch Saladin! If you'll not thank him, I'll ram my sword down your cowardly throat!"

"And I," said the prince of Sidon very distinctly, "will hold your arms while he does so."

The litter lurched nearer, bearing with it, to the imagination at least, a smell of corruption.

PART III

The Politicians

1192–1193

Two DAYS before Christ's Mass a minstrel wandered into a small town on the outskirts of Vienna. He did not sing in the marketplace, being French-speaking and in any case superior to the ragged crew thumping tabors who were already performing there and begging for pennies. This man was warmly dressed, though stained with travel; and he carried a viol on his back, which proclaimed he had some skill. Though he did not by any means look like a court musician, he probably at least could sing for his supper in small baronial castles whose rough owners cared less for music than for novelty.

It was market day when he appeared, strolling casually up
to a crowd which was gathering to listen to a man preaching
a new crusade. This speaker was a hoarse-voiced fellow, one-
eyed and villainous-looking, who had taken the Cross, he
said, on account of his sins.

For all his appearance, he had considerable eloquence as
he waxed warm on his theme. When Saladin had taken Jerusalem, he had ordered the Holy Cross to be scourged
through the streets. In outrage, kings and princes had vowed
to recover the city for God. King Philip of France, King
Richard of England, old Red-Beard, the Emperor, even their
own suzerain lord Duke Leopold of Austria had taken the
Cross and gone beyond seas, bearing with them as glorious a
train as ever was seen. But the faith of these great ones had
proved impure. They had treated with Saladin, exchanging
presents with the sons of the Devil. After rescuing Acre and
the other coastal cities, they had turned their backs on the
Holy Land to return to their own quarrels, leaving Jerusalem
in infidel hands. God would restore the Holy City only to
simple people who took the Cross in faith, vowed to give no
quarter and accept none.

His audience heard him out until he started to call for volunteers. At this point the minstrel turned to one of the
men standing next him to ask in a heavily accented German
if he were not tempted by the promise of salvation. The
rustic hawked and spat. Nothing daunted, the minstrel
nudged another and repeated his question, adding:

"You look like one who has experience of fighting."

This second man, who was a thickset fellow in a worn

leather jerkin, lifted his sword hand to show the minstrel that he had three fingers missing. "Lost 'em at the siege of Acre," he grunted, "in the train of our Duke Leopold." He spat in his turn. "I've *been* on pilgrimage . . . with him . . . and him . . . and him!" He jerked his thumb. "Let the preacher go if he wants to fight harder than we did."

Now this, it appeared, was what the minstrel had hoped to discover. His new friend must know that tales of the crusaders were an important part of his repertoire. But those who had been on crusade were frequently impatient of verses made up by men who knew little about it.

The old soldier grunted dubiously. He had met French-speaking men among the men-at-arms of King Philip and King Richard, but the quarrels of his superiors had bred suspicion. After a pause, he replied in surly tones that if the minstrel had need to know about the Crusade, it was a pity that he had not taken the Cross himself. He looked a nimble fellow.

The minstrel winked and nudged him again. "Indeed I took the vow; but Spain was nearer, and for a little price I bought permission to fight the infidel there. Salvation is all the same wherever it is won; and Holy Church has the contents of my purse, which must have otherwise gone to the Venetians or the Pisans for my passage."

The old crusader grinned, rather pleased that the minstrel should get salvation at half-price. Besides, he himself had crossed with the Venetians and was glad to think that they had been cheated out of a passage. The ice being broken, he consented to adjourn to an inn where they could discuss the Crusade over a noggin of ale. An hour or so later, he and three of his cronies, who had gathered like flies at the merest hint of refreshment, were telling the minstrel a number of disreputable stories, which he received with laughter.

"I perceive that you are all adventurous fellows." He slapped his hand on his knee. "No doubt you even saw Saladin close enough to describe him."

Red William, it appeared, had loosed an arrow at Saladin as he galloped around the camp at Acre, a little man in a white cloak on a gray horse. They all knew he was Saladin because of the pennant which had been carried before him; but the Devil, alas, had protected his servant from that arrow.

The minstrel beat on the table with his leather mug to signal for more ale, and the host came over with a jog. "At all events," he heard the minstrel saying, "you must often have seen King Richard the Lion-Hearted at Acre, and you can tell me what kind of a figure he was. Did not even Saladin send him a fresh horse when his own was killed beneath him? Ah, King Richard is a hero of whom songs are sung!"

The host caught his elbow against the minstrel's shoulder and slopped beer on the table. He mopped it up with his sleeve, muttering curses in a steady stream. No one else said anything. Indeed, the very mention of King Richard had frozen the company.

"Even more than before, men are asking for news of King Richard," pursued the minstrel, ignoring the glowering looks directed at him. "It is many weeks since the King sailed homewards, and yet he is still looked for in his fair Duchy of Normandy and his kingdom of England. Little joy has his mother, Queen Eleanor, this festal season! Some tell her that her son is sunk without trace, while others whisper that he was taken while crossing some enemy's lands and has vanished into a dark dungeon, whence he may never again see light of day."

"In God's name," cried the host, setting down his jug upon the table, "what have poor men like us to do with King Richard? May the Devil fly away with him, say I!"

The minstrel grinned. "Now perhaps you have the truth of it, for who else would dare lay hands upon a pilgrim returning from the East? The Holy Father has laid a terrible curse on any man who does so. Worms shall eat him, and the fires of Hell shall consume him forever!"

There was a dead silence in which the chatter and bustle in the rest of the smoky room fell loudly on the ear. The host looked at Red William, who had absentmindedly refilled his cup from the jug at his elbow without paying. William put a hand to his belt and took out a knife which he turned over in his fingers with the air of one who did not quite know what he ought to do with it.

"What King Richard looks like I know," continued the minstrel, ignoring William, though his own hand went to his belt beneath the table. "Indeed, his is a common type among us Normans. In my home town of Rouen there was a knight called Walter Leroy who was as like to King Richard as two peas are in a pod. Men said he was a bastard of Henry Plantagenet, so that the two were half brothers; but his mother would never admit the relationship."

"There was no such knight on the Crusade," said Red William shortly.

The minstrel smiled. "No doubt he went disguised, for King Richard kept it secret that there was a man who could pass for himself when need arose. Well as I knew Walter from boyhood, I could never be certain which one was the King, if it were not for a single token which marked the difference between them."

The host, still hovering behind the table, frowned at William to put his knife away. A thought seemed to have struck him. "What was the difference between the false king and the true?" he demanded, leaning suddenly forward to insert his broad shoulders into the circle lit by a sickly candle on the table.

"Why, that is simple." With the smoothness of a professional storyteller, the minstrel looked around him, gathering attention. "The King wore on his finger an emerald set in gold which had descended to him from his grandmother, the Empress Matilda. No green jewel of this size could be found to match it, but the King had a ring made for Walter with a red stone which he might wear in its place. This stone served as a warning to those who knew Richard well."

"It was the red ring!" exclaimed the landlord, too horror-struck to contain himself. "I saw it on his finger. He said he was a merchant, but you said — " he jerked his thumb at William, "and you — and you — and you — You all said he was King Richard in disguise and that Duke Leopold must know of it. What will become of us now?"

There was a horrid pause as the rustics stared at one another, reflecting on the anger of Duke Leopold, which was evidently nearer and more to be dreaded than the curses of the Pope.

The minstrel deliberately raised his eyebrows. "Now if a fair, tall man came to this hostelry calling himself a merchant, why should you not believe him? Is it likely that Richard Plantagenet would trust his person, even in disguise, to the lands of Duke Leopold, whose banner he tore off the walls of Acre and flung into a sewer?"

The landlord looked around him with belated caution. The minstrel had deliberately drawn his new friends into a corner, while they in their turn had discouraged others from joining their group lest the minstrel run out of funds to pay for ale. What with the professional patter of a palmer selling relics straight from the Holy Land as a cure for the murrain which was presently on the sheep, what with coughing and stamping from those coming in from the cold, and calls for more beer, the room was noisy enough to cover conversation. He bent forward, thrusting his face across the table to within a foot of the minstrel's.

"There was a rumor," he said in a rapid murmur, "that a ship had been wrecked on the coast and that some great ones, who did not give their names, had come ashore. Days later there appeared a big, blue-eyed man with two attendants and wearing a ruby in his ring. So weary was he with spurring that he lay three days like one dead in my hostel, while his beast was so worn out that it could no longer go." He spread his hands in a helpless gesture. "What is the King of England to me, or who am I to risk the displeasure of our

Lord Duke? On the third day, William here climbed a ladder to look into the room where they all lay in my best bed." He pointed at William accusingly. "You swore he was the Lion-Heart in person!"

"So I did, and so I do," said William stubbornly. "I saw him a thousand times in the camp at Acre."

"No doubt you did, my friend," agreed the minstrel. "But how often did you see King Richard there and how often his double? Tell me that!"

William was not so easily bluffed. He persisted sullenly, "He confessed he was the King when they came to take him, nor would he surrender save to Duke Leopold in person. We laid no hand on him until the Duke rode out from Vienna. Well pleased was he to see his enemy in his power! They put him in the midst of a company and fastened his bridle to that of another knight as they rode away. Nothing was said about a double then."

"And if this man were not the King," put in the landlord, taking heart, "then where can the King be? Richard of England cannot cross Austria without being recognized by many others who knew him as well as William ever did. Where is King Richard?"

"Ah, safe in Saxony by now," argued the minstrel. "See now, he sent his double hotfoot to Vienna to draw off pursuit, while he more heavily disguised and better attended went by a different route. It would be wise of you all to hold your tongues, lest Duke Leopold discover that he has been cheated. These great ones do not like to be made look foolish."

It was plain that the company was really frightened. Beer mugs stood forgotten on the table while they stared at each other aghast. "I will do my best to keep the matter secret," promised the minstrel, who had his own excellent reasons for wishing to prevent gossip. "It is never prudent for humble folk like ourselves to meddle with the quarrels of the great ones. Perhaps we should not even be seen talking any longer." He lifted up his voice in a drinking song which he had learned in one of the taverns in which he had already been following certain rumors.

It was a catchy tune with a good chorus and a number of dialect verses, each more indecent than the last. The audience began to beat time, join in, or shout appreciation. Under cover of the convivial atmosphere, it was little noticed that William stumbled out, his cronies after him, or that the landlord filled up mugs in gloomy silence.

The minstrel slept in the best bed that night with two companions, and as well as he could he ran his hands across the mattress and fumbled underneath it. He found no trace of earlier occupants except fleas, of which there were many. Perhaps partly for this reason he got up early and took a draft of morning ale to speed him down the dark, cold, muddy track towards Vienna, which he reached at sunrise as the gates were being opened. He accosted a packman coming out to ask him if he would take a message to Worms for two gold pieces. Since this was equal to a whole year's profit, the pedlar was eager. The minstrel gave him a single coin and promised another would be forthcoming on prompt delivery. He was to seek out a Frenchman in the suite of a certain bishop who had come out from England to the German Emperor. He was to say to him: "The leopard hath the lion. Now let the eagle be swift to make his claim."

Duke Leopold was holding Christmas court at Vienna with mumming plays and games of blindman's buff or forfeits. Presents were being given and received with gay flirtation. Dishes were brought into the hall preceded by trumpeters and outlined in flickering brandy. Jugglers, minstrels, and fools entertained the company, the court performers striving to add to their repertoire lest it become stale. These last were not best pleased at the arrival of the minstrel, who had bought himself gay clothing with gold ducats he had concealed in the lining of his viol case. To the lords and ladies a French-speaking man was especially welcome, for the lays of chivalry had their birth in France.

The skill of the minstrel soon won approval. He could sing a story of Sir Gawain at King Arthur's court to set the ladies sighing, and follow it with the tale of a mouse rescuing a lion to make the men laugh. Young folk, who called for the latest love songs, found him able to pour out their pretty rhymes and delicate tunes in endless flow. In fact, all agreed he was one of the famous troubadours, though he denied it with laughing face, calling himself Niemand, which means No One. Rumors went around that he was a knight, even possibly a prince wandering in disguise for love of adventure.

However this might be, the minstrel could not stop singing. He was even found in the courtyard outside the great keep of the castle entertaining the varlets there with a song composed by King Richard, who was a troubadour himself and loved minstrels about him. It was tactless of him to have singled out King Richard for mention in the court of Duke Leopold, and one of those who had heard him from a room in the keep thought it well to murmur a hint. The minstrel thanked him, but that evening after supper he chose for the court a tale of the Holy Land.

When the infidel conquered Jerusalem and swept over the kingdom like an irresistible wave, Prince Reynald of Sidon left his castle in charge of his seneschal and went to surrender to Saladin, whom he quickly charmed by his conversation. So learnedly did the prince discourse of Arabian poets, and even of the Koran, that the sultan imagined he would become a convert to Islam. Reynald spun out time pretending to make up his mind, while his seneschal quietly strengthened his castle and stored it with provisions. At last Saladin perceived that he was being fooled, and he sent the prince under escort to his own gates, bidding him order them to surrender under peril of his life. Then Reynald shouted to his men on the wall in Arabic, telling them to surrender; but in French, pretending to translate, he told them to hold fast. The castle did not fall, but Saladin was too wise to be deceived. He had learned, however, to love the prince, so that he forgave him, keeping him as an honored guest until he was ransomed.

It was a pretty tale to please the ladies, but Duke Leopold listened with a lowering brow, remarking that the sultan liked generous gestures to cover up his evil deeds. No doubt Saladin had wished it forgotten that he had hewn off the head of Reynald of Chatillon with his own hand when he was captured.

The court sat silent, all being aware that Duke Leopold hated to be reminded of the Crusade, where his reputation had been overshadowed by his enemy Richard of England. But though the Duke glowered, he sent the minstrel a gold ring. Furthermore, he roused himself to say, albeit harshly, that most of the songs of the Crusade concerned King Richard.

This almost open invitation was so startling that even the chatter of the squires and serving men died down. Everybody stared at Duke Leopold, who sat twisting the stem of his wine cup with a grim smile as he prepared to listen.

The minstrel was too wise to take up such a challenge. For once, he said, his repertoire had failed him. Instead of a story he would favor the company with King Richard's own song. He made it ring through the silent hall and echo through the warren of passages which led to the kitchen and premises he had never explored. Nobody thanked him, while the duke abruptly called on tumblers for entertainment.

Next morning the minstrel was gone; and some days later another message came to the Bishop of Bath, who was attending the Christmas court of Henry Hohenstaufen, the German Emperor, to whom he was kin. It said simply: "The leopard hath many lairs where his prey can be hidden."

Without the minstrel, New Year festivities in Vienna lacked spirit, the more so as there arrived a messenger from the German Emperor, whom the Duke received with a display of anger. "How should I know where King Richard may be? No doubt the Devil has his soul, while his body rots in the wreck of his ship, God only knows where. How can I give him up if I do not have him? Someone has been telling my liege lord false tales about me?" He presided over his banquet with lowering face, while the messenger went back to the Emperor empty-handed.

The minstrel, meanwhile, was singing King Richard's song in a remote Alpine castle to which he had made his way through a snowstorm. His throat was sore and his voice ragged, but the Duke's castellan in such an outpost was not critical. Luckily his lady was a motherly soul, delighting in hot possets and bitter medicines. But though the minstrel's face was flushed next morning and his voice the merest croak, he would not stay longer.

On Twelfth Night he trudged through the bitter cold while the Emperor Henry took counsel with the Bishop of Bath, who came away shaking his head. Another messenger had come to his lodging with the words: "The Alps are empty."

"Pray God King Richard be not done to death before we find him," murmured the Bishop to the Frenchman, who was his secretary.

"Duke Leopold does not guess how the news traveled," said the other consolingly, "and the uncertainty will prevent him from acting."

"He fears the Emperor, but hates the King." The Bishop sighed. "Which passion will prove stronger?"

"Leopold is a greedy man," the secretary retorted. "He is already tempted by a share in the ransom which he knows the Emperor will get for the King."

No doubt this view ought to have cheered the Bishop, but it was depressingly true that the most he could do for his master was to transfer him from one prison to another. Henry Hohenstaufen and Philip of France would strip the King like vultures, even though the Pope excommunicated them both for the detention of a pilgrim returning from the Crusade. Excommunication, like the Crusade itself, was grown too common! The Bishop turned with a heavy heart to composing a letter to old Queen Eleanor and the regency council in England.

The minstrel was avoiding the Duke's important castles. There were too many people in such places to keep a secret well. More primitive strongholds were remote, however. He was footsore and saddle sore, and his arm had lately been wounded in an encounter with a robber who had tried to cut his throat in a wayside tavern. Sorely he was tempted to rest, but he was driven with the same sense of urgency that pressed on the bishop. It was too easy to bury the King under the stones of his dungeon if it seemed wise to swear he had never been seen. Duke Leopold might prove a man to whom revenge was dearer than ransom.

The Castle of Durrenstein, rising grim and savage from a great rock which overlooked the Danube, was a military outpost rather than a residence, used for collecting tolls and controlling the river. Little had been done to its ancient keep since the days when a baron's stronghold had been as crude as a peasant's shack even if more durable. Since then, the outer walls of Durrenstein had been strengthened by round towers, but the castle yard, or rather midden, was still surrounded by stables and other huts of mud and wattle in which the only cheerful sight was the glow of a furnace where a smith was shaping a shoe for one of the horses.

The minstrel had come to Castle Durrenstein as to other castles of its kind, his German repertoire much enlarged by primitive ballads about feuds and murders which he had picked up in his travels. Professional gaiety, though second nature to him, failed completely in the songs preferred by men-at-arms whose true calling was robbery with rape, or even torture.

The gatekeeper was glad to see him. The shivering groom who held the horse for shoeing grinned from ear to ear. A dirty scullion sneaked out from a lean-to kitchen at the base of the keep, one slight improvement since the days when the meat was roasted in the hall. Part of the garrison emerged rubbing eyes as though late sleeping and midnight hours were common to some in this castle. The minstrel treated them all to a running patter in which he passed on the gossip of the region. Emperor Henry, it was said, would come to Ratisbon. A pretty maiden had been found dead in the miller's dam at Grünwald. A two-headed sheep had been born on the lands of the white monks outside Munich. A pious beggar had been healed of blindness by washing his eyes in Saint Walpurga's well. Richard of England, the rumor went, was held secretly in Austria. He glanced around him and saw that his audience looked startled. Smoothly he slipped into one of the hoarse chants of the region.

The door of the stair at the bottom of the keep flung open, and a young man hurried out, unkempt and loutish, but yet superior to the men-at-arms by reason of a silver buckle on his belt and a worn furred cloak which had most probably formed part of plunder taken from some merchant. Correctly judging him to be the son of the castle's lord, the minstrel brought his tedious song to an end and began to tout superior wares.

"Fresh from the court, my noble lord! The very latest from the Christmas court of the Duke in Vienna. Need I say who sung it there?" He winked, impudently laying a claim to which his costume and manner gave the lie. Even if the young oaf did not believe him, his appetite for tidbits from the great world would be whetted.

Uncouth though he was, this young man showed ambition. Perhaps he thought he might pick up a fashionable tune or get the minstrel to teach him foreign words. It was almost too easy, thought the minstrel, tuning his viol for the twentieth time to play King Richard's song.

He always gave this song the full range of his voice, sending the music soaring as lightly as his frosty breath on the winter air. Occasionally a man with a musical ear would listen with mouth open, but the young heir of Durrenstein was not of that class. Clearly he had no idea that he was hearing a king's favorite whose golden notes were famous through Normandy, Anjou, Poitou, and Aquitaine, the lands of chivalry, and all the other dominions of King Richard.

The minstrel came to the end of his verse and paused, continuing the melody on his viol. Without warning came the moment for which he had waited. From the slitted tower a rich bass voice took up the strain, carrying on the poem which no one knew in this land save its author, King Richard.

The minstrel gave a start, so that his fingers wavered on the strings of his viol, which uttered a strange screech. The door at the foot of the stair opened at the same instant, and out of the corner of his eye he glimpsed the figure of the lord of the castle, one hand on his sword as he listened to the music.

The lips of the minstrel smiled, though they felt stiff. "Why, I see you have a musician already, and not a bad one, though he lacks polish. Let me try him with another verse." He lifted his voice again. He had long ago prepared a verse in the French of Provence, which was a dialect unlikely to be understood in these rude parts, even if an old crusader knew some French.

"Oh, my King," sang the minstrel, "is all well with you? If bribe or trickery can win you escape, a boat, a sword, and a swift horse will be at your service. If not, the overlord of him who owns this place shall claim your person."

"No bribe or trickery will set me free." The confident voice rang almost as richly as it used to do in Richard's own hall. "Men guard me with drawn swords night and day in this small room. Let the overlord make claim; I fear not him. He is only — " The message ceased because the singer had come to the end of his verse, so that his opinion of Henry Hohenstaufen could not be uttered.

With the gaze of the lord of the castle fixed upon him, the minstrel dared no more. He shouted hastily in German, "Well done indeed, thou unknown! Now have pity on a poor man and be quiet while I earn a night's lodging!" He did not like the grim faces of the men-at-arms in the court, nor the discomposure of the lubberly son, who was staring up at the loophole in the keep with his mouth open. If that boy were to say anything imprudent, there might be one less minstrel in the world — or one less king.

Perhaps the lord had the same thought, for he said sharply, "Adalbert, where are your wits?" The boy jumped, but he shut his mouth. The father advanced a step towards the minstrel saying, "The singer is my older son in bed with a broken leg. Adalbert! You had best go in and keep your brother company."

"B-but — " began the boy. Then thinking better of it as he met his father's frown, he moved sulkily past him and into the door of the keep, which he slammed behind him.

"You were saying," remarked the lord, turning back to the minstrel, "that rumor declares King Richard is held somewhere. Now that tale interests me! Where can you have heard it?"

His tone was calm, but the minstrel felt hair rise on the back of his neck. The lord of Durrenstein was a heavy man, once blonde, now faded in color, with a manner which felt rather than looked as though it were dangerous.

"Oh, in the taverns of Vienna!" The minstrel winked

confidentially. "Rumors spawn about King Richard because he has vanished. It is not for me to question a tale which wins me welcome from people like your lordship."

The lord smiled vaguely, but his dull eyes still measured the minstrel, while his hand lingered on the hilt of his sword. "You have a certain skill which is wasted on the courtyard. A Frenchman of your sort will usually hang around great houses instead of begging his bread from door to door."

The minstrel shrugged sullenly, gathering his wits. To claim great connections would invite suspicion, but an obscure man might well be killed and buried just to insure against risk. "To tell you the truth, I have a weakness for liquor which has cost me the favor of Duke Leopold. I have taken a vow to drink no wine till Easter, by which time the Duke will be searching everywhere for Niemand with the golden voice. Meanwhile, as it happens, I am a man who likes variety." He added as though in haste, "This vow of mine takes no account of beer."

The lord seemed to make up his mind. He took his hand from his sword hilt to beckon a man whose badge of office was the key to the buttery hanging at his belt. "Fetch him ale, but small beer, mark you. He's not to be drunken before he entertains us after supper."

The minstrel gave careful thought to which songs would be prudent that evening and most in keeping with his character. To his surprise, however, the lord sat over his wine without calling for music, ignoring his dough-faced wife and his thick-lipped son, and only showing awareness of where he was by occasionally kicking the dogs for growling over the bones thrown under the table. After a while, he began to talk, rehearsing the outlines of a long grievance without pausing except for an occasional nod from the minstrel.

All evil stemmed from the Crusade. Knights had mortgaged their lands for passage and equipment. Later they had sold their rights to pay for ransom or had been stripped to the bone by greedy neighbors snatching what they could while the owner was away. And for what had they suffered? Where had the money gone? To greasy traders grown rich from ferrying pilgrims, men who squabbled for concessions in Acre as soon as it had been rescued by the blood of fighting men. Ah, how eager those merchants were to deal with the infidel and make their profit out of buying and selling Eastern wares! Yet they were unwilling to aid the cause of God except for payment.

What of the palmers or purveyors of relics? With his own eyes the lord had seen one of such people cut the forefinger from a dead infidel, which he had later sold as the finger of Saint Thomas with which he probed the wounds of the risen Lord. By the Mother of God, there were three forefingers of Saint Thomas in the Duke's land of Austria, all vouched for by Holy Church, which grew rich on their miracles of healing. From the keep of Durrenstein one could look down and see how the roads swarmed with burghers, traveling merchants, holy frauds, and Jewish usurers, who dared not venture abroad in his father's time. Like moths they had consumed the riches of an honest knight who had struck his blow for true religion, only to starve like a mouse trapped in a cupboard smelling of cheese.

"There is a devil in this man," thought the minstrel, aghast. The lord of Durrenstein was weaving King Richard into his tirade, accusing his arrogance of breaking up the army. Richard's treaty with Saladin had left Jerusalem in infidel hands, reduced the barons of the country to landless men, and bankrupted knightly pilgrims who had come overseas to win fiefs in the kingdom.

The minstrel listened, nodding occasionally as the sense of the argument demanded. He was thinking: "There is no knowing what such a man might do, whether orders came from Vienna or not. Any night when he is drunk he might go up the stair of the keep with his sword in his hand and murder in his mind." He wondered how early he could get away tomorrow and under what pretext, whether he could hire a horse to make more speed, whether Emperor Henry was still at Worms or had come to Ratisbon. He clasped his hands on his lap because he felt them tremble.

Emperor Henry came to Ratisbon, and the Bishop of Mainz, who traveled with him, proceeded down the river to Vienna. Here he was closeted in secret with Duke Leopold. "The Emperor demands the surrender of King Richard into his hands, for this same King has done him much injustice."

Duke Leopold struck the arm of his chair in seeming anger. "How can I surrender King Richard if I do not have him?"

"Then if not King Richard," said the counselor, looking the Duke in the eye, "you shall surrender Durrenstein."

Leopold started, and red rushed into his face. For a full minute he propped his chin on his hand and stared at the

Bishop, while he turned the matter over in his mind. "Who told you," he demanded at last in a tone which boded ill for someone, "about Durrenstein?"

The Bishop shook his head, for he honestly did not know. "The Emperor will pay you a share of the ransom," he promised.

"How much?" retorted Leopold, preparing to sell his captive dear if he could not retain him.

The Bishop returned to Ratisbon with an agreement signed and sealed; but Duke Leopold with twoscore men-at-arms rode down to Durrenstein, where he demanded to know how the prisoner had been guarded and with whom he had spoken. Here the visit of the minstrel had not made a great impression, for traveling entertainers came and went; and indeed at the moment that the Duke arrived there were a pair of them in the courtyard.

"If he was never alone and spoke to no one, he must have bribed one of the guards." But the lord of Durrenstein swore that none of these was ever alone with the prisoner. Why, he himself on his occasional visits always had two men in close attendance, for King Richard's strength was dangerous.

"By God, I will know the truth of this," swore the Duke. He was tempted to put the lord of Durrenstein to the torture. The lord, however, was less sure to know the answer than one other man inside the castle. He went up the stairway to the small room where they were guarding King Richard.

King Richard sat in the only chair and looked at his enemy. He was a big man with red-gold hair and blue eyes, his skin yellow as the tan of the eastern sun faded in the dimness of a small, cold room lit by a single loophole. His clothes were worn and a little threadbare, and he had huddled a rough blanket around his shoulders. Yet there was no mistaking the air of a man who did not need to put himself forward because he was and always must be first.

Duke Leopold sat on the bed because he would not stand in the presence of his captive. Richard raised a sandy eyebrow at the gesture, but said nothing.

"You will go to Ratisbon," said the Duke abruptly. "The Emperor Henry has many an account to settle with you!"

Richard showed neither surprise nor concern. He merely remarked mildly, "Well, an emperor's welcome should be . . . warmer than this mousehole!"

"Who took your message to him?" demanded the Duke. He balled his fist and struck it on his knee. "Let me warn you, I *will* have an answer!"

"Little man" — the King looked down his nose — "dukes do not take this tone with kings. With emperors, for all I know, it may be possible."

The Duke scowled, swelling with hatred for his careless, arrogant captive who had not even the sense to be polite. He had tortures at his command, and kings were no better than any other man when it came to the question. But Richard was not responsive to threats. The Emperor Henry, he pointed out, would expect to receive him in proper condition.

Duke Leopold glared at this reminder. He knew he could not face the outrage of the Church, his overlord, or even his people if he treated King Richard like a common criminal.

It might cost him his dukedom, he thought, fuming.

"By our Lady," he swore, "there are poisons which do not kill a man immediately. There are also fevers and plagues which are said to cling to a sick man's bedding. King Richard of England might go to Ratisbon in good health and might there sicken. . . . In Jerusalem there was a leper king, as I remember."

One could not have said that King Richard went pale because his color to begin with was not good. Nor did the air of arrogance which was natural to him diminish, but he sat perfectly still to think this over. Presently he turned his head and let his glance flicker at the door, where the two guards were standing. "Send them out. They may wait on the stair."

"What do you want?" he demanded when the two were out of earshot.

Duke Leopold showed his teeth. "Who betrayed your whereabouts? His life or yours, O King."

"Swear on the cross of your sword that you will deliver me to Ratisbon unharmed, and I will tell you."

Duke Leopold swore. It pleased him that the King had fallen so low out of fear. This triumph would console him for a hundred slights. He would have the guilty one torn to pieces in the courtyard under the King's window. He could hear how clearly the song of the minstrels came up into the room.

Richard smiled at him dazzlingly as he gestured at the loophole, through which the toneless chant in the courtyard could be heard. "It was my minstrel Blondel, who sang the tune I made for him beneath my window. You should have caught him when he entertained you, for I do not think he will ever venture to Durrenstein again."

The Money-Makers

1204

W E CANNOT AFFORD IT," protested the Lady Margaret of Boisvert to Sir Eudes when she had him safely to herself behind the curtains of their bed.

Eudes grunted angrily and twitched the coverlet, taking more than his share to show that he meant to be master. "Will you never cease to blame me because the sun shone in my eyes in the lists at Troyes? Was any knight never unlucky? Must I stay at home the rest of my life to pay one forfeit?" He turned his back on his wife and buried his head in the pillow.

All this was unfair of Sir Eudes, as both of them knew. It was not the ransom of his horse and armor which had strained the resources of Boisvert, but the actual expenses of attending four great tournaments last summer. "You'll need a fresh tent," persisted housewifely Margot, "with your coat of arms upon it. Silk of course. Then spears and a second charger. So many expenses! Those changes needed in your tilting armor cannot be done by John Smith in Boisvert. Young William has grown out of all his clothes again, and none of the grooms looks fit to attend you. Your green gown will not do. The fur on it is nothing but fox from our own woods." She sighed slightly. "My gowns are all too tight."

"You'd best stay at home," said Eudes savagely, "and save expense."

Dead silence fell while Eudes feigned sleep, half glad, half sorry. Margot dried her eyes on the edge of the coverlet, trying to take consolation from the fact that his suggestion showed good sense. With her dumpy figure, snub nose, and sallow complexion, Margot looked out of place among court ladies, and dressing her up was a waste of time. All the same, it was painful to discover that Eudes could manage without her. They had always passed for a devoted couple because Margot had a fund of practical sense on which Eudes depended. She had brought him a comfortable dower, including the manor of Beaupré, which bordered his own. She had borne him two daughters and a snub-nosed boy who was the apple of his eye. But still he was restless.

Eudes's only fault in Margot's eyes was his romantic

yearning to make a figure in the world. Most luckily he had no turn for flirting with court ladies; but he had set his heart on becoming champion in all the tournaments of the countryside. Boisvert was a modest fief, so that the prizes or wagers which Eudes brought home were never equal to his debts. Margot had learned to stint; and she dreaded the visits of the Sub-Prior of the great Cistercian abbey, always anxious to drive a hard bargain in return for a loan. As long as she dared, she had remained silent, perceiving that she had no glamor to console her husband for the loss of the excitement which he craved. Now that she had spoken out, Eudes went off alone, leaving Margot to plan retrenchment with the anxious steward and to set her maids at letting out old gowns.

Young Thibaut, Count of Champagne, who was holding the tourney, had a fancy to lead a new Crusade. The kings who had vowed to wrest Jerusalem from the grip of Saladin had thought more of their quarrels at home than of doing God's business. They had returned with their work half done, leaving the holy kingdom shrunk to the island of Cyprus and a few Syrian ports. Even King Richard had forsaken the cause and come home, to die in a petty quarrel with one of his French liegemen. The thoughts of the faithful turned back to the First Crusade, whose pilgrims had been lesser lords without great involvements in Europe. Pope Innocent had sent a preacher to France, one Fulk of Neuilly, whom Thibaut invited to speak to the knights assembled at his castle. Those who took the Cross and remained for a year in the army were to have forgiveness for all the sins they had committed, provided that they confessed with a proper repentance.

When Eudes came back to Boisvert with the Cross on his shoulder, Margot fell weeping into his arms. They were not a couple who indulged in foolish fondness, but Eudes clasped her and even shed tears in his turn. "I did it for your sake," he said, "to win our fortune."

In the next few months Eudes was exalted and regretful, eager and homesick, proud of his castle and vain of his quest. Margot soon dried her tears and showed her pride by smiling on the Sub-Prior when he came to talk about another loan.

Tournaments had been extravagant, but the Crusade was ruinous. Even Eudes was dismayed at his expenses. Margot secretly showed her jewels to a traveling Jew, who shook his head. All the ladies in the land were selling such trinkets, so that the price had fallen shockingly. Margot put them away again and wore them defiantly when a neighbor who had taken the Cross rode over to tell Eudes what arrangements had been made about the journey.

Each pilgrim, he reported, was to make his own way to Venice, where the Crusade would assemble and take ship. The Venetians had promised transport for horse and man, supplies, and fifty war galleys, all for a price. How much each knight would have to contribute was uncertain, but Eudes for once was in despair. "If I have to mortgage Boisvert," he said to Margot, "however will you live?"

"You had better sell Beaupré," said Margot calmly.

"Anne's dowry and little Eleanor's provision for entering Saint Margaret's nunnery! How can I do that?"

Margot put a good face on the matter. "You shall buy it back with the riches of the East."

Eudes brightened up. "That's true! God pays His army with the plunder of the infidel. In a couple of years, we'll all be rich!"

Even when Beaupré was sold, it was only by careful contriving that Eudes was able to set out. Luckily Abbot Thomas of the Cistercians, who was a great lord and intimate, it was said, with the Holy Father, had decided to go with the Crusade. It suited him to pay the expense of a few valiant knights as far as Venice, since the foothills of the Alps were full of robbers who might not respect even his holy person.

Eudes rode away in the following spring. As soon as he had left her, Margot stripped the castle of the tapestries she had worked with her own hand and the silver goblet that Count Thibaut's father had given to his godson. The carpets that had come from Beaupré, the painted book of hours which had belonged to Margot's mother, the cellarer's best wines, the very spices from the kitchen all went, some of them to the nuns of Saint Margaret's convent, and others to traveling merchants who were still swarming over the countryside to snap up bargains. Every vestige of comfort which Margot had kept for Eudes's sake, all display proper to her rank was sold, until the castle was as grim and bleak as in the days when it had consisted of a stone keep and a wall with sheds against it. Thus provided with a little ready money, Margot fought to save Boisvert from outright ruin.

Eudes, meanwhile, was caught in a similar struggle. The army was not as large as had been hoped, since numbers of pilgrims had preferred to sail in their own ships. Those who assembled in Venice could not nearly pay the sum agreed upon. Leaders gave up their gold and silver plate, while knights like Eudes stripped their equipment to bare bones; but nothing sufficed.

Without full payment, the Venetians would not release their transports, nor the sailors they had hired, nor the war-galleys which they had promised as escort. Meanwhile, the army camped outside the city, growing ever deeper in debt to Venetian merchants for provisions.

Enrico Dandolo, the Doge of Venice, was a fitting leader for this town of hardheaded merchants. To be sure, he was incredibly old and almost blind, so that people led him about by the hand and secretaries stood behind his chair to read him papers or guide his pen to where he needed to sign. Yet no one could suppose that Dandolo was lacking in energy or wit. Old age had merely dried him; pride had stiffened his very wrinkles. Dandolo was greedy, not for himself, but for Venice. The city was built on trade — trade with the Syrian ports which were the remnants of God's kingdom; trade with Egypt, where Saladin's heirs grew rich from it; trade with the Queen of Cities, where the Venetians preyed on growing weakness. From Christian, infidel, and Greek, the wealth of the East flowed into Europe through the port of Venice.

From this Crusade, as from all else, Dandolo looked for profit. Why not? Since Venice served God, was it not right that God reward her? No merchant might so much as trade with the East without bringing home treasure to adorn the cathedral of Saint Mark for the glory of God. Doge Dandolo was ambitious to give Saint Mark greater spoils than ever.

"If these pilgrims cannot pay," decided the old Doge, weighing the matter, "then let them earn their passage. Let them take Zara and pay us out of the spoils they get from it."

Great tumult arose in crusader ranks because the town of Zara, which the Venetians coveted, was subject to the King of Hungary, not only a Christian, but one who had taken oath to join the Crusade. "We came hither," protested the Cistercian Abbot Thomas, "to serve God, not to slaughter other Christian men."

This was all very true; but Abbot Thomas had not contributed his silver plate or sacks of money to the cause, declining because they were not his, but God's and the Order's. He had continued to live and dine like a prince, while the bulk of the army was at wit's end to find means of buying provisions.

"Either we go on, or we go home," clamored men-at-arms who, having invested little but themselves in the cause, lost little by desertion. Sir Eudes of Boisvert, like many another more deeply involved, heard this cry appalled.

"I promise my lady to buy back Beaupré," Eudes confided, for the sale of Margot's manor lay heavy on his conscience. If he went home without even the money he had taken with him, he would bring ruin on Boisvert. Besides, the Holy

Father might fasten his sins, for which he craved forgiveness, to his back for all eternity. The fires of Hell were real to Eudes, and he shuddered. "We should be the laughingstock of Christendom," he pointed out in conclusion. "Better buy Venetian aid by taking Zara than face the collapse of the entire Crusade!"

It was the custom of the Doge to ask consent from his people for measures determined beforehand by the Grand Council. Not aspiring to the difficult task of using their brains, plain citizens were satisfied with the ritual of this act and shouted their applause with genuine feeling. On the Sunday after an agreement was signed for the taking of Zara, the huge cathedral was crowded to the doors. Outside on the square, thousands waited patiently for the criers to repeat their Doge's words. Among the crowd stood those who were to man the slim war galleys, the great transports, the clumsy provision ships, the shallow barges for the horses. Half Venice was engaged to go with the Crusade, provided, naturally, that the men received their pay and the merchants made their profit.

Dandolo rose from his chair of state inside the cathedral and, leaning heavily on the arm of his son, passed in slow motion across the choir to the lectern. Here he fumbled carefully with his foot for the steps, prolonging the business of handing him safely into his place. Gripping the rail with both hands, he stared at the huge audience with eyes still bright as though he saw them clearly. Silence fell as he breathed deeply, gathering energy to make his old voice heard.

"Lords," cried the Doge in a high voice, "you have with you the finest people in the world." He threw out his hand in the direction in which he knew the crusader knights were sitting. "You come for the greatest affair that people have ever undertaken." Once again he paused, drawing breath for another effort.

"I am an old man and weak; and I have need of rest and am enfeebled; but I see that none would be able to govern and guide you save I myself, who am your lord. If you agreed that I should take the sign of the Cross to guard and teach you, and that my son should remain in my place to protect the land, I would go to live and die with you and the pilgrims."

Men cried their assent with great emotion as the Doge, descending carefully, brushed aside the arm of his son to grope his own way to the high altar, behind which an altarpiece of Byzantine enamel focused the splendor of the vast cathedral in a blaze of gold and jewels. Tears stood in the eyes of many as the old man fumbled slowly past the choir. Was he not going to die far away from his home for the sake of his people? Dandolo knelt safely at last, and the priests put a cloak around him with a great Cross on the back, that all might see it. Others pressed up behind to take the oath with their leader.

All this the Doge did in public. Privately, to his son and the members of the Council he talked about money. "We have to get our investment back, and these lords will need watching." He rubbed his aged cheek in a thoughtful gesture. "There is talk among their leaders of sailing against

Egypt because the strength of the infidel lies there. I need not tell you how great a damage this would do to peaceful trade. By going in person, I may yet give this Crusade a better direction."

People nodded, and this time every eye was hard and dry.

Margot of Boisvert, joggling about her lord's land on a rough pony, had found the monks of the great Abbey pitiless towards her peasantry, whose feudal obligations Eudes had mortgaged. Gathering not for themselves, but for God, the monks forgave nothing. Wherever she could, Margot ransomed animals or sticks of furniture; but though this brought blessings, it also attracted more demands. Presently there was nothing to be done but seek an audience with the Prior to whom Abbot Thomas had entrusted rule in his absence. It might be possible that she could make an arrangement to pay him by degrees.

Only after many heart-searchings did Margot get up her courage to visit the Abbey. She knew her gowns were shabby, her hands red, and that there were strands of grey in her wispy hair. But when the Abbess of Saint Margaret's told her that a letter had come to the Prior from Abbot Thomas, eagerness for news overcame her reluctance. She departed from the castle early the next morning, arriving at the Abbey about the dinner hour, for it was winter and the ways were foul. The Prior sent out word he would not see her.

Margot was tired and wet and hungry. She sat down on a stone bench in the porter's lodge, letting tears roll down her sallow cheeks and drip onto her dress. The porter, a round-faced, kindly soul, fussed over her and brought a mug of wine. Margot, still weeping silently, refused it.

"It is because of the excommunication," said the porter, apologizing for his Prior. "Abbot Thomas — "

Margot sat upright, startled. "What do you mean?"

The porter glanced around him. Big with news and naturally a gossip, he lost no time in telling how the crusader host had sacked a Christian city. In grief and anger at such sin, the Holy Father had laid an excommunication on the army. This news had come direct from Abbot Thomas, who had not ceased to reproach the wicked pilgrims.

Margot fasted and wept before the little altar in the chapel of Boisvert. It was a wet winter, and her feet were swollen with chilblains until she could hardly bear her shoes. Eudes, quartered in the half-ruined town of Zara, fought with dysentery. Most of the plunder had gone to pay the Venetians, so that Eudes had not been able to support his grooms, who had left him for a wealthier knight. Luckily he was still welcome at the table of Abbot Thomas, who continually spoke out for going to the Holy Land. Since, however, the wintry seas were dangerous, the good man did not venture to set an example.

Even the lifting of the papal ban brought little cheer. The Venetians had not been forgiven; but in the palace where Dandolo lived in considerable splendor, it mattered little whether mass was said or not. The Holy Father would come around, Dandolo said. The immediate question was whether they could afford to go to the East. The Venetians had been hired for only one year, of which summer had been spent doing nothing in Venice, autumn and winter in Zara. Without assurance of more pay, the Venetians would hold to their bargain and go home in a few months.

Once more Dandolo put forward a scheme. A young prince had recently arrived in the camp who was the son of the late Greek Emperor Isaac, now deposed, blinded and imprisoned by his brother. This prince Alexius was a beautiful young man if one cared for an effeminate style, and related by marriage to some of the princes of the expedition. Dandolo had taken him up and had driven a hard bargain with him. For elevation to the imperial throne in the Queen of Cities, Alexius promised two hundred thousand marks in silver, a fabulous sum which would pay the Venetians and leave much over for the support of the army. He would also send ten thousand warriors with the crusading expedition. Thereafter, for as long as he lived he would keep five hundred knights in the Holy Land to defend what they won.

Even Abbot Thomas was tempted by so vast a bribe, reasoning that the cause was not unrighteous, since in the eyes of the canons Alexius was clearly the true heir. Besides, vague promises had been made of his converting the Queen of Cities to the true Catholic Church. A few of the clergy still demanded sternly that the host fulfill its vow instead of meddling with the affairs of another Christian city. Since these found no way, however, to hire sufficient transport, men more experienced in great affairs spoke for a treaty, which was duly signed under Dandolo's conditions.

The Christian host set out in spring from Zara, the Venetian men-of-war parading proudly behind the great red gal-

ley of their Doge. In one of the big transports propelled by
oars and sail, Sir Eudes had hung his shield on the rail
brightly emblazoned with the oak which was the coat of
arms of Boisvert. The sun shone brightly on the fleet, picking out the gay banners and the gilding of the great stern
castles. Sails swelled. Oars rose and dipped in regular
rhythm. They were off at last. Men assured each other that
the cause was good and their reward would be sufficient to
rescue all from the straits they had fallen into.

Spring came to Boisvert, also comforting Margot by the
news that the papal ban was lifted from the army. Lambing
had been good; and because there was a sheep murrain
through Normandy and Aquitaine, wool prices had soared.
The peasants mustered a little cheer at the spring plowing
and the blessing of their apple trees. Boisvert lay in an en-
clave, bounded on three sides by the lands of the great Abbey
and on the fourth by Beaupré, now in the hands of Margot's
brother. Thus the manor at least was free from the maraud-
ers who were wont to prey on the lands of absent barons.
Margot spent peaceful days driving her people to better
husbandry. Eudes would have been shocked to see her
brown and weatherbeaten; but his return was still far off,
while debts were ever-present.

The Queen of Cities was a marvel to Eudes, even though
by now he had heard descriptions of her. No words could
convey the actual impact of her vast double wall, over which
the cupolas of palaces and churches rose up the height of
land. By now, however, the imperial domains were sadly
shrunken by attacks from infidels to the east and Christians

to the west. Many of the trading ships in the huge harbor were foreign, most often Venetian. The soldiers were hired men because the best recruiting grounds were conquered. None of these mercenaries cared for their emperor any more than for his brother, or for his nephew whom the Franks wished to impose on the city. What use to fight with spirit for worthless rulers? Summer wore on, and the prince Alexius was made Emperor of the East with his blind father sitting useless on a golden throne beside his own for the sake of appearance.

In the city, Frankish knights wandered the broad streets, staring at the shops, marveling at the churches, or casting envious eyes at the incredible palaces.

"Alexius says that he cannot pay what he promised," grumbled Eudes. "Of course he can pay. Look at it!" He gestured at a fountain either plated or else of solid gold which stood, not even in the palace, but in the grounds of one Murzuphlus, who was husband to one of the royal princesses. "All these nobles bowed before their Emperor, faces down on the floor! Don't tell me he cannot take whatever he wants from them! People say he spends money like water on his banquets and jewels and scents. Doge Dandolo told him when I was there in the train of Abbot Thomas . . . 'We made you emperor,' the Doge told him right out in front of us all. 'And we'll unmake you unless you pay.' Roughly he told him, and the young fool went pale as a corpse. Not even nerve enough to answer back, and he an Emperor! Emperor!" Eudes made a scornful noise. "All these Greeks are alike!"

In this last statement he was wrong. The Queen of Cities had too much pride to be bullied, even if her worthless Emperor did not. It was easy to seize Alexius and Isaac, set up Murzuphlus in their stead, close the gates of the city against the Crusaders camped outside, and rouse the populace to lynch such foreigners as dwelt within the walls.

The Queen of Cities had asserted her dignity; but she was not able to maintain it under the rule of a man no better than Murzuphlus, who fled like a coward when the crusaders assaulted the city. Even the mighty walls needed better defenders than hired soldiers who had served three emperors in one year — all of them worthless.

The Queen of Cities fell with fire and sword and rape and plunder. The hoarded riches of centuries were exposed defenseless to men drunk with priceless wines and red with slaughter. Frankish men-at-arms ripped damask hangings, shattered crystal goblets, splintered delicate tables inlaid with ivory, gorged themselves with sweetmeats, and paraded clumsily dressed in silken robes or sacred vestments. Many seized on the women cowering in corners, tearing rings from their fingers or pearls from their hair. Knights used their swords to pry plates of beaten gold from priceless statues, silver hinges and latches from open palace doors. Jewels were stolen from reliquaries, bullion from the very garments of the Emperor.

In the great cathedral of Saint Sophia, soldiers hacked out pillars of solid silver, seized the chalices, forty in number, and the censers of pure gold, the silver candelabra, the covering of the altar, and a great table thickly set with precious stones. Even Abbot Thomas and his brother clerics joined in the plunder, greedy for treasure of a different kind. Here were the gold caskets containing the gifts that the Wise Men brought to Jesus, the tablets of law that were given to Moses, the trumpets before which the walls of Jericho fell down. The true home of such relics was in Catholic Christendom among the faithful, and there were plenty for all. In the Emperor's palace alone stood thirty chapels with pieces of the True Cross, the spear which pierced our Lord, the nails that were driven into His hands, not to mention bones and relics of the Saints beyond all counting.

Constantinople, bulwark of Christendom, lay defenseless and gutted. Frankish barons and Venetian merchants seized her palaces and crowned a new Emperor, Robert, Count of Flanders. Saint Sophia echoed with the chants of the Roman rite. Doge Dandolo laid claim to three-eighths of the Empire, deliberately choosing the islands and ports which would benefit Venice.

The Sub-Prior brought this joyous news to Margot, hastening to Boisvert with the flattering deference of one who knew all debts would now be paid. "By the blessing of God," exclaimed he, "our pilgrim army has brought the East under the rule of the Holy Father, to whom Our Lord entrusted the keys of Heaven!"

Margot frowned at him, a little puzzled. She had been interrupted at the candle-dipping, and her old gown was splashed with wax. "Then will the pilgrims set out for Jerusalem at last?" asked she.

"Jerusalem!" The Sub-Prior spread his hands in indignation. "With a whole Empire to conquer! With Greece and Asia Minor to be reconciled to the True Church! God has set their hands to this work, and they will not turn from it. The Holy Father has given solemn thanks for their victory in Saint Peter's."

Margot smiled, completely relieved of care. She beamed on the Sub-Prior. "I thank you, Brother James, for bringing me the best news that I ever heard. We have nothing but small beer . . . for we prefer it," she added, head held high. "Yet I cannot let you go without refreshment, for we must drink to the day when Sir Eudes comes home."

Small beer was not to the Sub-Prior's taste; and he had other views for Sir Eudes, whose manor of Boisvert would round off pleasantly the lands of the Abbey on the southern side. "Dear Lady, is it likely that Sir Eudes will come back while fiefs for the asking are to be gained in Greece and Barbary? So gallant a knight as Sir Eudes will win himself place with the great ones. When you go to reign as Duchess of Sparta or Athens, Boisvert will be nothing to you!"

"Sir Eudes is lord of Boisvert," said Margot tartly, "as our boy will be when he is grown." She frowned, picturing Athens as a great castle crowded with ill-mannered servants and pert young damsels, all fashionable people, among whom she would be out of place. "Nor can I stand chattering while my cauldron cools. But I thank you for your courtesy, Brother James; and I will tell Sir Eudes how highly you regard him." She curtseyed with a stumpy dignity and moved away, keys jingling at her belt.

Margot proved right and the Sub-Prior wrong. Both, how-

ever, were equally stunned by the announcement in Abbot
Thomas's next letter. For the present the Abbot remained
in the East, since high ecclesiastics of the Catholic faith were
hard to find, though the fields were ripe for the harvest.
Nevertheless, the good man was not unmindful of his Abbey. Under the care of the valiant knight Sir Eudes, he was
sending a treasure beyond price which God had granted him
to lift with his own hand from the wall of the Emperor's
chapel. This was no less than the very sword of Saint Peter,
wherewith he had struck a blow for Our Lord's defense in
the garden, slicing off a servant's ear. Except for the True
Cross and the nails that fastened it, or the garments of Our
Lord, there could be no relic in Christendom of greater
power. There was some need for haste in this matter, added
the Abbot in cypher, lest the Holy Father, Saint Peter's heir,
demand this relic. For this reason, Sir Eudes would depart
without delay and arrive before winter.

Margot looked with some dismay at her wardrobe, in
which there was nothing fit to greet Sir Eudes. Her children were clad in cut-down clothes and old hose, roughly re-
footed. The jubilant Sub-Prior offered a fresh loan now that
Sir Eudes was rich with eastern spoil; but Margot would
have no more dealings with him. She made her way to Saint
Margaret's convent, where the nuns were glad to leave their
stitching of new altar clothes to contrive what they could.
The Abbess even brought out Margot's jewels. "I bought
them in your need," she said, "to keep them for you."

Tears stood in Margot's eyes, but pride still stiffened her.

"I will borrow them gladly," answered she, kissing the Abbess, "until Eudes redeems them."

The scrawny horses of Boisvert were groomed with loving care, their harness oiled, their buckles burnished. There was much washing and mending of cloaks or doublets, repair of weapons, and even cutting of hair. No hasty applications of rosewater or milk could undo the ravages of work and exposure on Margot's hands or complexion. She did not look like a great lady, but she could tell Eudes how much debts had been lessened now that the harvest was in.

The monks set out from their Abbey after Prime, winding in long procession down the river which flowed through their domains. Ahead of them the sacristan bore a cross encrusted with gems which had been given to the Abbey by Margot's mother for the good of her soul and her husband's. Behind this rode the Prior on a mule with crimson trappings, accompanied by the Sub-Prior and other officials. Next walked the monks, two and two, followed by the lay brethren who did the menial work within the Abbey. After these rode Margot with her children and attendants, her brother, the lord of Grandpré, and various other barons who held lands near the Abbey. At the rear came the peasants of the domain in holiday costume, mingled with beggars hopeful of alms, sick seeking a miracle, and packmen or entertainers, who scented profit in a general holiday. At the border of the Abbey lands there was a ford in the river, beside which stood a little chantry, founded by the lords of Grandpré, in which daily masses were said for their souls. Here the monks had planned to receive their treasure. So well had the scouts stationed by the Prior done their business that the procession winding down the river soon saw another, approaching from a scrubby wood across the ford.

The monks raised a solemn chant, while many of the rustics dashed down the riverbank to get a view. Margot shaded her eyes with her hand, gazing eagerly over the heads of the monks to see if Eudes had brought his black charger home from the wars. But Eudes was not riding ahead, clad in mail and bearing his pennon with the oak tree of Boisvert. He was not even jogging along on his traveling hack, clad in the green gown which he wore on state occasions — for silver and green were the colors of Boisvert. A man walked ahead carrying a great black cross behind which came a procession on foot. A scarlet canopy carried in the middle on poles presumably sheltered the relic, while shading it from view. Behind came rabble.

Margot felt a tightness at her throat, a sense of disaster. Where was Eudes? Without a word to her brother, beside whom she was riding, she turned her horse along the riverbank among the rustics, who were running alongside the column of monks, almost drowning the sound of chanting by their cries of excitement.

The black cross advanced into the ford, its bearer disdaining to lift his long robes out of the water which swirled up his calves. Without hesitation the procession followed, its red canopy swaying in the midst of it, carried — yes, certainly carried by four men-at-arms in green with silver badges! To be sure, the two nearest Margot were utter strangers, black-bearded men with a foreign look. Where was Eudes?

The two processions were preparing to meet, the Prior on foot with his officers — their mounts discreetly removed to the rear — and the monks ranged in a wide semicircle around them. The black cross came out of the ford and halted, its bearer uncertain what to do. His followers came untidily to a stop, and in the shuffling, Margot saw Eudes.

He was under the canopy, until now concealed from her vision. Eudes looked gaunt and brown, unrecognizable to careless eyes, but not to Margot's. His long hair falling to his shoulders, which had been gaily curled when he rode away, hung straight and lank, its color faded to an indeterminate shade, half brown, half silver. Eudes, always so careful of his dress, had nothing on him but the long white shirt which penitents wore. His bare feet, though washed clean of dust by the river, were bleeding. In front of him he carried a scarlet cushion, in part supported by a leather strap around his neck. On it lay a short sword, heavy and broadbladed, dark in color, without any sort of ornament save a baldric studded heavily with precious stones and fastened by a clasp which looked like gold. Eudes did not look about him, as a man might do returning from war, but fixed his eyes only on the Prior waiting to take possession of his treasure.

The Prior was a handsome man with a smooth manner and an eye for good effect. He rose to the occasion with a speech that was neither long nor short, adorned with Latin tags, and yet not tedious. After praising God for His grace to the Abbey, Abbot Thomas for his care of the flock, and

Sir Eudes for his faithful service, the Prior advanced to take the sword, while around and behind him the brethren struck up a Latin psalm.

At this point the ceremony broke down, the canopy bearers interposing staves to prevent the approach of the Prior, while Eudes exclaimed in a loud voice: "I, Eudes of Boisvert, servant of God and His holy Church, have taken oath to travel barefoot from Constantinople to the Church of Saint Thomas belonging to the Abbey of Grandpré. Therefore let no one touch this holy relic until I have laid it there upon the altar."

The psalm died away, and the Prior went crimson with anger. Nor had he a chance to regain his dignity, for Eudes's procession had already started to move past him, pushing purposefully through the crowd of monks, which had to part and let it through. After a moment the Prior followed, while the monks re-formed in confusion, uncertain whether to begin the joyful hymn which was to have attended the reception of the relic by the Order.

Margot, trotting behind, had no answer for her brother when he growled that the thing had been an ill-managed business and that Eudes had made himself an enemy. Stealing a glance at her averted face, he added more kindly, "My purse is at your service if the Abbey presses you. It would not suit me to have the monks swallow Boisvert any more than it suited my father when he gave you and your dowry to Sir Eudes."

Margot knelt near the door of the Abbey church, trying to pray while Eudes went up to lay the sword upon the altar.

The monks could raise their song of joy at last, while Eudes, rising from his knees, came down the chancel, leaving traces of blood from his bare feet on the cool stone. His eyes looked for Margot. With courtly grace he took her hand and kissed it. Then he laid his own hands on the children's heads as they knelt for his blessing, while people made a little space about them. One of Eudes's hands was badly scarred and misshapen. He caught Margot's eyes upon it, and said gently, mindful of the ring of curious faces, "My tilting days are over, but I may yet serve to teach our boy to uphold the honor of Boisvert."

"It was a horse's hoof," he told her later, sitting on the edge of their bed while she undid the bundle that the servants had brought up from his packhorses. "Cut down and ridden down by our own men on the threshold of the Emperor's chapel! Thank God I saw no more of what was done there!" He shuddered. "I have seen a stricken field and had my share of fighting. We sacked Zara, and what we did there was not for ladies' ears. But Zara was nothing to Constantinople — nothing! . . . Here, give me the russet. I had it from a merchant who was about my size — in Zara, that was. A good cloth, and he had no further need of clothing. In Constantinople — " He paused.

Margot shook out the russet hose, looking doubtfully at Eudes's feet which she had washed and bandaged. Eudes took a stocking from her and began to put it on, with his good hand working it clumsily over the linen strips around his foot. Sitting thus with his head down he said, "How is it with Boisvert? I left you straitened."

"It is well."

"They divided up the spoil," said Eudes, with his face still hidden. "I was given my share in jewels so that I might travel lightly, for I could do no good in the East without my sword hand. There are rich fiefs to be won, but I was never lucky — "

"It does not matter," Margot said. "We have Boisvert."

"These jewels — " Eudes was not even pretending to put on his stocking. "They came from the vessels of gold which stood on the high altar. I put them . . . well, I put them in the baldric of the sword, except for the pearls. There had to be money for the ship and the escort and, well, the procession. And then we never did perform our vow, though it is time we were absolved from it. You see?"

Joy and dismay flooded over Margot, so mixed that she could not distinguish one from another. Somehow the riches of the East and Eudes had never seemed to go together. He had returned penniless and was ashamed. She said warmly, "Best give back to God what was God's, for the lords of Boisvert were never thieves."

Eudes took Margot in his arms and kissed her, while she laid her head on his shoulder and wept. Presently he said, "I am poor, but at least I have not come back empty-handed. I have brought us a holy thing which will do more for us than all the jewels stolen from God's altar." He fumbled with the strings at the neck of his shirt and showed her he was wearing a shell-shaped locket of beaten gold. "It lay under me when my men found me at the entrance to the chapel; and the Abbot bade me keep it back when the spoil was divided, saying that a relic may not be valued like common gold. We will hang it above the altar at Boisvert to bring a blessing on us and on our heirs forever."

Margot gazed on it with awe, afraid to touch it, lest she defile anything so very holy. "What is it?" she breathed.

"It hung in the chapel beneath the sword of Saint Peter. It is the servant's ear!"

The Innocents

1218

As CHILDREN streamed into Marseilles, sun shone brilliantly over wet roofs and gleaming cobbles, freshening the colors of this shabby, touching procession. Ahead of it went the oriflamme, the scarlet, swallow-tailed banner which good Saint Denis had entrusted to the kings of France to be their talisman. The boy who carried it was clad in scarlet from head to foot, his costume the loving gift of pious parents who had entrusted their only son to the children's army. There was mud on his scarlet hose; his fine jerkin was wet with rain and stained by sleeping on the ground. Notwithstanding, he was a handsome lad some twelve years old and made a brave show for all the watching women.

Behind the oriflamme, a group of boys rougher in appearance pressed around a cart drawn by two donkeys and decorated with green boughs and a medley of bright garments. Beneath a canopy which still dripped slightly sat God's chosen child on a cushion of velvet, quiet as an image, lurching only with the movements of the cart across the cobbles. Stephen was a dark-haired boy with a thin, brown face and an assurance of manner which the blessed Saints in church could not have bettered. His hands lay clasped on the lap of the rough sheepskin which he wore, in shepherd fashion, with the wool turned inward. His gaze was steadily upward, fixed on Heaven.

Behind him walked the children of France, clustering in companies, each group led by another scarlet banner. They were of every sort, these banners, rough homespun faded by sun and rain, or silk still bright with costly dye. The children, too, were of every kind: fair children, dark ones, children in rags, in homespun, in good broadcloth, stout twelve-year-olds and little ones no more than six plodding onwards hand in hand with older sisters. They marched not in hundreds, but in thousands, while treble voices challenged the children of the town to follow God.

Women clutched their young ones to them. Fathers of families darted dark glances at their offspring, previously threatened with the thrashing of a lifetime if they dared run after Stephen. Already, however, bold spirits plunged into the midst of the marching groups, whose members opposed their bodies with practised ease between them and their parents.

"Oh ye of little faith!" called out a young priest whose skinny frame looked gigantic amid the children with whom he was walking. "Will you forbid your sons to follow God?"

This was too hard a question to answer. All knew that mountains could be moved by childlike faith; but one's own Hugh or Raoul, an imp of Satan with well-known faults which needed much correction, was not the sort for whom the waters parted or weapons dropped from infidel hands. No one replied to the young priest, though many crossed themselves in awe. Women cried out when an exhausted child collapsed at their feet and then staggered up again, repulsing helping hands with feeble gestures. "God has called me, and in faith I can still walk."

"Where do you come from?" cried soft-hearted mothers. Most shrugged off the question; but some wept, and a few answered with the names of villages nobody had heard of.

"Where are you going?" cried the tall priest, gesturing forwards.

Childish voices in a swelling treble which passed down the street began to cry, "Jerusalem!"

William the Pig, who was in the crowd up near the front because anybody who knew him thought it prudent to get out of his way, caught the answer of the tall priest to a question and stood on tiptoe to mutter it into the ear of Iron Hugh, the chief of his captains.

"Walk through the water!" exclaimed William. "Did you hear him? They are going to walk to Jerusalem right through the sea. By the power of faith!"

Iron Hugh threw back his head, guffawing with laughter.

There were many others who scoffed, and yet when Stephen stood up in his cart in the marketplace to tell the people how God had called him, he commanded uneasy silence. The boy spoke like a messenger of God, promising to divide the waters with an assurance vaguely impressive even in a seaport town. There were holy priests in his train and some pious pilgrims, simple people who made no claims for themselves but followed the children. The presence of such adults made the boy's claims more credible.

William the Pig and Iron Hugh had gone about their business, for the truth was that they were engaged on an important matter which the arrival of the children had interrupted. Thus as the good citizens of the town threw their houses open to the crusaders, William the Pig with Iron Hugh beside him was entering an alehouse down by the docks, a shabby spot marked only by a dried bush hanging from a pole next a horn lantern, which was at this moment out as though the place were not open for business.

Ali the Sicilian was waiting inside with one of his captains, each wearing a cutlass and two knives in his belt. The landlord brought them a jug of ale and tactfully found occupation in the cellar. The four bargained in low murmurs, sitting on stools on either side of a dirty table, all careful to keep their hands in sight and away from their weapons.

The Sicilian wanted too much, as William had known that he would.

"My captains will not accept such terms," said he, feigning hesitation to draw the other out.

The Sicilian smiled, and the gleam of the tallow candle picked out the whiteness of his teeth. "My men will soon convince them."

William thought it prudent to show alarm. His big bulk quivered. "We came under safe-conduct."

The Sicilian waved his hand with careless satisfaction. "Go as you please, but by noon persuade your people."

William shifted a little, concealing relief. It was evident to him that the Sicilian preferred a treaty to a war. This being so, he would be vulnerable to pressure. "Noon is too short a time," he said deliberately. "Nor do I think it wise for any Moslem to threaten waterfront war while talk is everywhere of holy miracles and infidel blasphemers. Why, if one of these children were to be murdered, as might happen — " he paused significantly — "no one could save a Moslem from the people."

"Our agreement," retorted the Sicilian in angry alarm, "was your idea."

"So it was," agreed William calmly, "on my terms."

The Sicilian snapped his fingers. "That for your terms! I'll give you a week."

William turned this over in his mind, concluding that for all his talk, the Sicilian was a pawn of his own men, who were more numerous than William's. It would come to war, but William preferred to fight in his own way. He temporized. "A week. I'll talk to my captains."

William and Hugh got up and managed to sidle out of the door without ever actually turning their backs on Ali and his captain. There was no one waiting to waylay them in the street, which clearly showed Ali had expected a surrender.

"The fool!" said William tersely.

Hugh put a hand on the short club whose iron head had given him his name. "Do we wait here for them?" he asked in a whisper.

William made a contemptuous sound. "The Sicilian is too cunning to leave through a door by which he goes in. There is a passage in that cellar which leads clear through six houses to an alley."

"How do you know?"

"The landlord told me."

Iron Hugh was silent; William the Pig had various ways of persuading men to do what he wanted. Besides, to reach the alley they had to follow a twisting route of some length; and William, despite his bulk, moved fast. He wanted to be in position before the Sicilian came out.

They brushed past an old watchman going his rounds with a lantern, but he knew William well enough to look the other way. His light, however, revealed strange scenes. Huddled on doorsteps with arms about one another for warmth crouched the flotsam and jetsam of the Crusade, the lame and the footsore who had crept into town as the gates were closing, and had sunk down to sleep in the open streets.

William kicked one whose legs were in his way and cursed him bitterly. "Devil take you, spawn of a — " his voice died off into muttered obscenities as he ran. What Hugh and he had come to do required no witnesses, and it was important that the alley should be empty.

Unluckily for William, a group of young crusaders had wrenched the shutters off an old-clothes stall at the corner of the alley. They had looted the interior and smashed up the boards to kindle a fire, over which they were roasting unpleasant shreds of meat. The owner of the stall, one of those Moslems who, like the Sicilian, infested the port, had thought it wiser to put up with his losses. Thus the little alley in which a dark deed was supposed to be done was as full of people as an alehouse, besides being lit with leaping flames and improvised torches. William the Pig halted outside the range of the lights to curse with renewed energy.

"By God and all the Saints, if it were any other night than this, I'd ship the lot of you and sell you in Tunis."

"What a cargo!" agreed Iron Hugh, who knew from experience that a lively lad was a piece of merchandise which always got a decent price from the Moslem. "It'll be hard with us if we can't pick up one or two!" he added hopefully.

"And be hanged in the marketplace," snorted William in contempt. "One enemy at a time! We have war on our hands." He moved off, unwilling to be seen in a spot which would give away his knowledge of the secret exit and his ill intentions.

For three days Stephen lingered in the town while bands of stragglers staggered into a rude camp outside the walls, some sick and dying, others laden with plunder from the countryside. Here the guild of bakers set up ovens for them; tavern-keepers gave ale, rich merchants clothing. Even William the Pig, whose interest in the Crusade astonished all who knew him, loaded up a couple of hogsheads of salt beef on a cart and delivered them in person to the tall priest, being anxious to get full credit for his gesture. "Thomas is his name," he reported to Iron Hugh, "and he is sister's son to the Bishop of Beauvais."

"Then the Bishop's sister has borne a long-faced fool," retorted Hugh, whose nerves were suffering because William had made no move to counter Ali and had not so much as discussed the affair with his captains. "I hope your victuals poison him," he added spitefully.

In the short time that the Crusade had lingered, young Thomas the priest had been conspicuous by height and energy, by holy office, and by his other-worldly piety. Few priests had followed the Crusade, and most who had done so were simple peasants of no account. The clergy of the town, instructed by their bishop, the monks in obedience to their abbot, and even the holy brothers of Saint Francis warned that miracles were wrought only by saints. Despite the innocent faith of many, practical citizens soon discovered that some of their guests were unblushing thieves. Hugh thought these had more wits than Thomas the priest, and he said so; but William, rubbing his fingers through his reddish hair in a thoughtful gesture, expressed the opinion that faith was useful sometimes. "You'll see," he promised.

On the third day, all the children, to the number of about

seven thousand, gathered in the marketplace or the streets that led to it, carrying bundles presented by kindly hosts and raising wooden crosses which were to be their weapons against the infidel. All faces were radiant because the hardships of the journey were expected to end when God parted the sea and took them under his protection.

Stephen placed himself behind the scarlet banner and led them to the harbor at a point where wharves made way for open beaches on which fishing smacks could be drawn up on crude rollers. This morning the stretch was empty of boats, for practical seamen had no mind to be swamped by the tidal waves of a mighty miracle. Stephen halted at the line of dried seaweed left by the last storm, while the children pressing behind him spread out along the same line as though it were a fence. Their scarlet banners kept them in rough order, which allowed them to form in an irregular mass along the seafront.

It was a fine day with a crisp wind ruffling the water into waves of a foot or so which broke a few yards off, sending eddies, neatly edged with foam, in the direction of the children. Meanwhile, the great breakwater, the quays of the town, the battlements, and even rooftops which commanded a view of the harbor were black with people. An hour passed while the children assembled singing as Stephen stood motionless on the line of seaweed. Those next to him later said that beads of perspiration stood out on his forehead as he gabbled the simple prayers that he used to say among his sheep.

"My son," said Thomas the priest, leaning forward to

touch him, "let us go forward in the name of God."

"In the name of God!" cried the boys around Stephen, raising their wooden crosses. The gesture and the cry ran down the beach.

"In the name of God!"

Stephen jerked back his head and lifted both arms in a sudden gesture. His mouth fell open as though he wanted to cry out, but no sound came. He took five running steps forward, halting at the edge of a receding wave, as though daring the water to return and wet his feet. When it did so, he stood still as a stone while it swirled around his ankles.

What he would have done or said cannot be known, for the excitement of the children had burst bounds. Screaming, calling, babbling every kind of nonsense, beside themselves in a frenzy of faith, they surged down the beach and into the water, ankle deep, knee deep, then through the breakers, those behind shoving and shouting that God was testing whether they feared to drown.

Soon younger ones stumbled and screamed and clawed at their elders. Others were shortly up to their necks and struggled for a footing on the gently shelving ground. Behind them, masses still pressed forward, crying that faith would force the miracle from God.

As the sea did not part, panic deepened, for those who strove to get out were pushed further in. Knots of children began tearing at one another, screaming and choking as they tried to climb on the bodies of their friends. In the shallows, a few lucky ones began to struggle out, collapsing exhausted to retch up sea water. One of these felt an arm on his shoul-

der and saw the tall priest bending over him, his garments
dripping.

"Get boats!" he pointed to the quays. "Tell men to get
boats and to bring ropes to the beach. The children are
drowning!"

Already the screams and the confusion had drawn helpers,
particularly from the waterfront. Ali the Sicilian passed fat
William hurrying across the beach with a rope on his shoulder. Ali said nothing, but held up four of his fingers and
shook them in William's face.

"Four days!" muttered Hugh.

"By God!" swore William, halting for a moment, "he'll be
sorry before the month is out that you and I did not manage
to cut his throat outside that tavern!"

He hurried on, and Hugh ran after him grinning.

The worst of the struggle was broken up by boats, and
ropes, and chains of fishermen holding one another by the
hand. Half-drowned children were laid limply down by
dead ones on the beach. About two hundred would go no
further on any crusade. Most straggled back into town, some
lost in tears, some sullen, leaving the seashore strewn with
crosses, while red banners floated in the surf where their carriers had dropped them.

Stephen would not retreat. He had rescued the banner
which was always carried before him and had planted it on
the beach. Standing beneath it, eyes red with seawater or
tears, he was repeating to everyone who came near him,
"God did promise. He did. I had faith, but the rest were
afraid." Gradually a hundred or so of the children came to

crouch around him, crying quietly as Stephen reproached
them.

"We were all afraid," agreed Thomas the priest, who had
taken two of the little ones on his lap, while others laid wet
heads against his shoulder. "God has shown us how hard a
thing is faith. He is training His soldiers for the day when
they must face an infidel more angry than this sea."

Stephen lifted up his face with the radiant smile which
had often won an audience. "Why, so He is! And though I
did not doubt His power, I was for the time cast down. Now
my faith is perfect again! God has denied us one miracle for
our good, but He will send another. If we are not to walk
through the sea — " He looked longingly at the ocean as
though God might relent, but the sparkling waves rolled in-
wards in unbroken lines to break on the beach. "If we are
not to walk, then we shall ride." He looked at the children
and shook his head. "God sees you are weary and footsore.
He has pity on you and will send us ships."

Stephen's new promise spread like lightning, for he hurried to preach in the marketplace from the very cart which
he had abandoned there. It was amazing how he put fresh
heart into the children, so that by the following day one
might have imagined the terrible scene on the beach had not
taken place. The people of the town, however, were less con-
vinced. To ask for shipping for a wild adventure and with
never a penny to pay for hire was an absurdity in a seaport
town. It might have been possible that God would part the
sea, but men made ships.

Thomas the priest went the round of the docks, but captains only shook their heads at him. "You'd best go home."

"We have no homes," replied the priest. "We follow God."

It was hard to make any answer to this. It had by now dawned on the people that the children could no more go back than they could go forward, since few had any idea in what direction their native villages lay. Meanwhile, the town's resources, already strained, could not be equal to supporting them for ever.

"God will melt your hearts," persisted Thomas the priest. "I will ask you tomorrow."

On the second day, he got ill looks and curses for answers. People resented being pestered to do what they plainly could not do, even for the love of God. They had their own livelihoods, their wives, their children to think of. Besides, they offered their regular candles to good St. Andrew, patron of fishermen. They paid for masses for the souls of men whom the sea had taken. In fact, their religion was a thing that did a man some good. It did not ask him to throw away his livelihood for an army of children who wanted all he had and offered nothing.

"Get out!" cried one of them roughly, clouting the priest so hard that he measured his length on the cobbles of the quay.

"For the love of God!" cried the priest despairingly, rising to his knees. "Will no one furnish us ships for the love of God?"

William the Pig, who had come down to the waterfront

both days to watch what went on, clapped his hand on a bollard with a sudden gesture of decision. "For the love of God, I will!"

The miracle of William the Pig made almost as big a sensation on the waterfront as a sweeping gesture on the part of God like opening the sea. When the first astonishment had subsided, men agreed it was obvious that William had simply taken leave of his senses. Since he had not enough ships to transport the pilgrims, it was taken for granted that he could not even carry out his promise. But Ali the Sicilian, though known to be a Moslem, soon announced he was venturing his ships, which together with William's might suffice if the children would put up with crowded quarters. William said he had hired Ali, but no one could imagine where he had laid his hand on the money to do so. Iron Hugh, who had taken no part in the negotiations, caught William as he emerged from mass to ask him bluntly what he was about.

"Our men are getting nervous," he remarked.

William scowled under his sandy brows. "They've been nervous for a month. Not one of them but was ready to give in to any terms."

"That may be," retorted Hugh with gathering anger. "But what are the terms? How can they sail with Ali without knowing?"

William glanced around him cautiously. "No place to talk about it in the street. Come home with me."

Even when he had settled Hugh in the front parlor which he used as a countinghouse, William took occasion to visit the shed where two maids were washing clothes and to discover that his sister, who kept house for him, was gone to visit a gossip in the neighborhood. Returning, he poured out wine for Hugh and sipped his own, drawing patterns with his finger on the scarred table where he did his accounts and paid off his captains. Finally he raised his lead-colored eyes and fixed them on Hugh. "Tell the captains that we share the profits of this venture in proportion to our ships . . . two parts to us and five to the Sicilian."

"*Profits?*" inquired Hugh, blankly astonished.

"Ali," said William deliberately, "plans to sell the children into slavery in Egypt. Do not tell our captains, lest they protest; but you may promise that if there are no profits, I will pay them for the voyage."

Big Hugh's mouth opened foolishly. In a general way he had no scruples, but crime on this scale overwhelmed him. To sell an entire Crusade into slavery was a conception which had not occurred to him. Nor, as he turned it over in his mind, did he like it. Since, however, it was not his habit to make objections to William, he was uncertain how to begin.

"But . . . why Egypt?" he asked weakly. "Tunis is nearer."

"Ali is Sicilian, and they have war with Tunis."

Hugh accepted this, merely shifting his ground. "Ali will never pay our people off. Why should he, five to two?"

William, unmoved, shrugged massive shoulders.

"It'll leak out," protested Hugh, gathering momentum. "One of our sailors is bound to talk. Besides, what will people think when our ships return, but nothing is heard of the children? We'll be burned at the stake for this! We'll be torn in pieces! It isn't worth risking for the riches of the whole East!"

William got up and opened the door to look in the kitchen, which was at the back of the house. He found it still empty. He sat down again, leaning forward with his face as close to Iron Hugh's as the table permitted. "Nothing will ever leak out," he explained in a murmur, "because ships and sailors will not come back. For all anyone will ever know, they and the children will have been lost at sea. This you will arrange in Tunis."

Hugh goggled at him in confusion. "Tunis? Egypt?"

"Ali thinks he is going to Egypt, where he has friends; but you will secretly sell Ali, together with all his ships and sailors and cargo, to the Emir at Tunis. We give the rendez-vous, and the Emir sends out his ships to gather them in. Allowing for his profits, there will be a fortune left for you and me."

There would be riches beyond dreams! There would be freedom from Ali and his demands without a war. Slowly a grin stole over Iron Hugh's face as he began to savor the scheme in all its beauty and completeness. "Old fox!" he said admiringly. "How did you manage to make the Sicilian trust you?"

William the Pig shrugged. "It was his greed, and — " He hesitated, pulling at the loose flesh of his cheek. "Well, to tell the truth, I had to consent that young Philip . . . er . . . that young Philip should be one of my captains."

Hugh made no answer because he could think of none. Young Philip was William's sister's son, besides being the nearest thing to an heir that William possessed.

"If Ali had won his war with us," said William fiercely, "they'd have cut young Philip's throat."

"I daresay they would."

"He's better off alive, isn't he?" cried William, tapping impatiently on the table with his fist. "I need you to do the bargaining while I stay here to keep Ali quiet. Will you go or won't you go? I tell you fairly, if you will not, I'll throw you to the Sicilian like a bone to a dog. Will you go to Tunis?"

Hugh had got his composure back. Young Philip was no concern of his, no more than the priest Thomas, or Stephen the shepherd boy, who would soon discover that it was dangerous to hear voices from God. Hugh and William would be rich beyond all dreams! By the bones of Saint Andrew, William the Pig might have become an emperor, had he been nobly born. The only flaw in the scheme was that they would never know what Ali said when he understood the fate in store for him. All the same, they could have Ali's price and give a feast with it which would be remembered on the waterfront for years.

"When shall I start?" he said.

Since most of the children on the Crusade had been village people whose parents lived out their lives within a few miles of where they were born, not many went in search of their vanished children. Of those who did so, fewer reached

Marseilles. The Bishop of Beauvais sent agents to inquire, as did the father of the boy who had carried the oriflamme, a merchant from Lorraine. By the time these men arrived, a full year had passed without tidings. William the Merchant, as he now preferred to be called, had paid for masses for the souls of his sailors lost in that expedition and promised a window to the new church of the Franciscans in memory of his poor drowned nephew Philip. To be sure, the inquirers picked up some nasty stories about William, who was said to levy tribute with threats along the waterfront. Clergy, however, praised him as generous to Mother Church. Many sins might be forgiven to a man whose money did much good. In the end, the inquirers returned to those who had sent them no wiser than they had been before they came.

William built himself a fine house befitting a rich merchant and courted the widow of a guildsman who brought him a position among the respectable elders of the town. His lady was pleased to observe how many men deferred to William, and she was proud of the chapter house he was building for the friars.

In this way for many years William prospered, indulging a weakness for fine furred gowns grotesque on his vast girth. Iron Hugh also grew rich and set himself up as a ship owner. Every so often, William brooded about Iron Hugh. The possession of a secret had drawn them into a partnership which had its dangers. Neither dared or desired to betray the other . . . but Big Hugh drank. Hardheadedly, taciturnly, yet continually he drank. One never knew.

It was not indolence which stayed William's hand, but an

indiscretion which he had committed himself when the
Bishop of Beauvais's inquirers had come stirring up the mud
around a secret which was not buried deep. In hasty alarm
he had warned Hugh that he had left a sealed confession to
be opened if he died. Ever since, he had wondered whether
Hugh had been inspired to a similar precaution.

The Children's Crusade was almost forgotten, and William's position in town was one of immense power. All the
same, though he was feared, he knew he was hated. An in-
discreet word might start ugly rumors spreading like a fire
underground. It was many years since William had used a
knife, but he had not forgotten where it went most easily
into a man. He measured Hugh with his eye as they sat
talking business, his mind on a problem of which he often
thought but never spoke.

A gentle tap on the door interrupted his train of thought.
William's confidential clerk thrust in his head to say that a
man had come in from the street with a message to William.

"What sort of man, fool?" demanded William sharply.
"Do we know him?"

The clerk hesitated. "Well, he is from overseas, but even
his mother could hardly know him now."

The man who entered the room was scarred and distorted
to a travesty of his natural shape. A great cut running across
his face had smashed the bones of it, puckering up the skin
and straining it into unnatural lines. His front teeth had
been knocked out so that he spoke with a mumble. His
whole person was bowed and shrunk together so that he
might have been an old man, had it not been for a coarse

black beard of scanty growth which partly concealed the outline of his chin and the damage to his lips.

Such sights were not uncommon after wars, and William glanced at this piece of human wreckage indifferently. "You have a message?"

The stranger leaned forward, bony hands on the table and his one remaining eye fixed morosely on William. "Not a message. Greeting." He spoke slowly, forcing the words through his broken lips with a painful effort to articulate. "Greetings from Egypt."

"I do not trade with Egypt." William was wary.

"Yet many know you there, including a slave called Thomas, who was once a priest."

Iron Hugh emitted a strangled snort, but William sat as though frozen in his chair. He was trying to trace the outlines of Thomas the priest in the man before him, but he could not do it. Surely his height had never been great, and his eye was too dark.

"Thomas is slave to a merchant with whom our ship did business," added the stranger in his careful tones.

William's heart was pounding as though it would break out of his chest, and he found it difficult to keep his voice even. This was a disaster about which he occasionally dreamed but, waking, refused to think. "Now why," said he with painful calm, "did you come here with this story?"

"Who would believe me if I spoke out? Thomas himself is well connected and of a character which would be trusted. It happens that his master is a good man who would set him free for a price. Perhaps there are many in Marseilles who would offer his ransom, but only one man who would pay much more to keep Thomas in Egypt."

William rubbed a sandy eyebrow thoughtfully while the silence lengthened out. "I see," he said at last, "that you intend to drive a bargain. Sit down, then, and have some wine."

He levered himself out of his great chair and padded round the table towards the dresser where his goblets were kept. He was still quick in his movements when he chose, and his hand had not lost its cunning. His knife went into the base of the stranger's throat just where he planned, going down as easily as cutting through butter. There was not very much blood, and he made no sound.

Iron Hugh leaped up in dismay. "He would never have come here without entrusting the story to someone for his protection."

William wiped his knife on the dead man's sleeve. "That may be so, but we must take our chance. He came because he wanted revenge, not money. It was Ali, the Sicilian. I knew his hands."

In the next six months, William's wife fussed to her gossips that her husband's hair was growing gray and he slept badly. Nothing happened, however, so that in a year or so William was able to do business with Sicilian clients without passing a hand across his brow to wipe off sweat. When three of them came to him with the most preposterous kidnapping plot he had ever heard of, he laughed it to scorn. The Emperor Frederick, young and energetic, was a terror to the lawless in his Sicilian kingdom, both Moslem and

Christian alike. He was also a thorn in the side of powerful neighbors, including the Emir of Tunis and the Holy Father himself, once Frederick's guardian, now darkly suspicious of whether he were even Christian. It was uncertain which of these were behind a nonsensical scheme to make away with him, but not for all the jewels of the East would William meddle.

The Sicilians went on urging. Their principals were too well known to manage this business, but William's connections reached far and wide underground. They had made up their minds that no one else could handle the matter.

William merely shook his head, not bothering to argue or tempted by the sum they offered, though it was enormous.

Their leader, seeing that he was not to be moved, fumbled at his belt, undoing a leather purse which hung there. "Take this then!" He threw it on the table so that a few silver coins spilled out of its mouth. "It is the ransom of a certain priest called Thomas, held in Egypt."

William's face went almost gray and he felt dizzy, so that for a moment it was obvious that he was deeply moved. "Who is this Thomas?" he demanded, but his voice sounded choked, rather than indignant.

The leader shrugged, indifferently. "Ali told us that you would pay all you had to keep him in Egypt . . . but Ali has vanished."

William saw that he was beaten, at least for the moment. "For such a price I might be ready to help you," he agreed.

William sent for Hugh and gave him certain orders. He dispatched messengers to agents in Sicily, in Naples, Tunis, and Rome. Among the five of them, the spiderweb of a vast plot took shape, even while William tidied up his affairs in Marseilles and spoke openly of business which demanded his presence in Italy. Nevertheless, he took some desperate precautions so that three days before he was due to sail, he came down with the smallpox. He had privately decided that it would be better to die in his bed than in the dungeons of an emperor who welcomed criminals as a chance for crude scientific experiments.

The plot being already in train, Hugh and the Sicilians left William groaning, in doubt as to whether he had made the wisest choice by courting infection. Weeks later, however, as he was supported into his countinghouse by a couple of stout servants, news was brought to him of the hanging of Hugh and the others in the market square of Syracuse. Locked in the chest behind his own chair was the leather bag with the pieces of silver which might have freed Thomas from slavery in Egypt. On the shelf with his own was a silver goblet of Hugh's from which he used to drink. William signaled to the servant behind his chair and pointed to it. "Take that away!"

William's wife complained that he did not recover from the smallpox. He had lost weight so that the skin of his face hung down in folds, causing his enemies to compare him to a toad, rather than a pig. With Holy Church, however, he was even more in charity than ever. His benefactions were extravagant; and he purchased indulgences for many grave sins, storing a pile of them in the chest which held the purse with the pieces of silver. They fortified him against Hell; but not against vengeance on earth, which haunted his dreams.

Only William knew how much it weighed on him that his spiderweb of connections had been torn apart by the struggles of too large a fly. After he lost three ships in quick succession from piracy, he was prompt to sell the others. He hired a couple of bodyguards, telling his wife that his heart gave him trouble, so that he dared not go out without servants to help him.

On the waterfront of Marseilles there were kidnappings. Bodies turned up floating in the harbor with stab-wounds in the back. Such indications of underground gang warfare had not existed for twelve years, since . . . now that people were discussing the matter . . . the time of the Children's Crusade. Of course by this time even parents must have forgotten the victims of that sad episode, for children died easily and human life was short. One man remembered them because he had to.

Fate knocked on William's door at last in a very gentle fashion. The servant who opened it saw a man who was long and lean and brown like a seafarer, a little stooped, in old and faded garments which must have come down through several hands before they reached him. His mouth was tight; his cheeks were dry and sunken; and his eyes had the wary look of one who had seen danger as a constant companion. It had been noticeable in the crowded street that he shrank towards the gutter, letting other men take the wall as though by habit. The servant, who thought him little better than a beggar, told him sourly that his master saw no one at this hour, for he was dozing.

"Your master will see me," replied the lean man with modest assurance. "My name is Thomas, and I come from Egypt."

"Eh, what?" grunted William the Pig through the inner door, which chanced to be open to get a breeze in the countinghouse. "Who's asking for me?"

Thomas raised his voice. "Seven thousand children demanding the vengeance of God."

Dumbfounded by this peculiar remark, or, as he later said, by a sense of horror, the servant stood aside, allowing Thomas to advance across the inner threshold and face William, whose arms were on those of his chair as though he were trying to get on his feet. For a moment there was silence.

"So you prospered!" exclaimed Thomas, taking in the polished woodwork, the Turkey carpet, and the chair cushioned in Cordovan leather. "They told me so, but I wanted to see with my own eyes. Did you ever hear children screaming in the night?"

William tightened his fingers around his chair, but his heart was pounding too strongly for him to get up. Like a cornered animal, he showed his teeth. "No, never."

"Did you never lie awake and dread the day, lest God should send one home at last?"

The knife was still at William's belt, but he was aware that Thomas's story would be known to all on the ship on which he had come. The man had walked openly to William's house in the middle of the day and had probably been followed by those who knew his errand. It was no use doubling and turning any longer. The truth was out.

With a fearful effort, he drew enough breath to speak and turned to his servant. "Throw this man out of doors, and leave me alone!"

The servant advanced to do as he was bid, but Thomas slipped around a bench, eluding him, as he declared an oath, like an apparition. He moved to shut the heavy street door, but paused, distracted by a flock of blackbirds which came chattering over the roofs and settled in a tree across the road. No doubt they were devils waiting for a soul, since when he turned back towards the inner room, William already had used the knife on himself to cut his throat.

The Saint

1298

On August the twenty-fifth in the year of Our Lord 1298, King Philip the Fair went in procession to Saint Denis to disinter the bones of Saint Louis. With great pomp he escorted these to Paris to lay them in the glowing chapel which Louis had built to house the Crown of Thorns and other relics bought at a vast price from Constantinople. Thus the royal Saint was lodged once more within the palace where he had lived and worked for the good of his people. King Philip ordered a golden reliquary to be made for the skull, encrusted with jewels.

The sainthood of King Louis was more than a tribute to his virtues. It was a symbol that King Philip had mastered the Pope in the long struggle for political power over Christendom. In the twenty-eight years since Louis's death, his saintly power had wrought miracles of healing, mostly by curing sick men after an appearance in their dreams. By a typical courtesy towards the poor and simple, he had miraculously dried a flooded cellar through the power in one of his old discarded hats. Never was there any doubt of his piety, of his death in the service of God, and of his goodness. In his lifetime, King Louis had towered head and shoulders above the common height, and after death he seemed more than mortal size to his people.

Proofs of sainthood had been amassed, but several Popes had proved unwilling to sanctify the father or grandfather of the ruling King of France. They felt it dangerous to give such spiritual claims to a political rival. Thus the final recognition of Saint Louis signified the decline of the Holy See and the power of King Philip.

King Philip's triumph was celebrated by a banquet over which he presided clad in blue and scarlet, his cloak powdered with gold stars and lined with ermine. His two brothers sat at table beside him, flanked by the greatest lords of the land and served by knights in tunics of silk. Lesser lords carved for the great ones and graced the table of Queen Jeanne, wife of King Philip and in her own right Queen of Navarre. The company was gay, for the King and Queen were not yet thirty, and Queen Jeanne liked to have bright faces about her. The King, though impassive as was his wont, wore a flush of triumph upon his handsome face. Courtiers who understood his mood hastened to mask his silence with their chatter.

Hugues de Bonville, Philip's Grand Chamberlain, was seated next to John of Joinville, whose position among men of higher rank on this occasion was a tribute to his great age and his intimacy with Saint Louis. The Sieur de Joinville was a small dried-up man with a face like a withered apple who made little conversation, partly because he came seldom to court and found the faces there strange, and partly because he was busy sparing his few teeth by munching slowly.

"By God's bonnet, he said so!" swore the Chamberlain gaily. "I heard him myself."

The Sieur de Joinville leaned courteously forward to take the Chamberlain by the sleeve. "If I may be so bold on our Saint's feast day," said he, inclining his head with old-fashioned grace, "I will venture to remind you that our beloved Saint Louis held all oaths offensive to God. In all the time I knew him, he never said anything stronger than 'in truth, it is so.'"

"Go to the Devil!" replied Sir Hugues shortly, for he was a favorite of King Philip and unaccustomed to reproof.

The old man's beard quivered with anger as he retorted, "I hold to the blessed Saint's ways myself. Anyone who swears by God or the Devil in the castle of Joinville gets his ears boxed, whoever he may be."

"God save me from the castle of Joinville!" cried Sir Hugues, leading his friends in mocking laughter.

The matter went no further, since a quarrel in the actual

presence of the King could not be thought of. The old man's
memory, though clear about the past, grew confused by the
present, so that he seemingly forgot the matter. Sir Hugues,
however, did not forget to grumble among his intimates
about the old fool of Joinville. One of these, Enguerrand of
Martigny, a man of mean descent but great ambition, was
eager to rise by favor of Sir Hugues. Accordingly, on the
next day he went swaggering over to the embrasure where
the old man at the Queen's desire had collected her pages to
tell them stories about good Saint Louis. After listening for
a moment or two, he broke in loud-voiced:

"Since when has it been the fashion for a servant to dress
better than his master?"

The old man stared at him, brows raised. "Sir, I do not
know you, but give me leave to say that when I was your
age, I did not venture to interrupt my elders."

Sir Enguerrand laughed easily. "Times change, old man.
In my day it is not thought fitting for a courtier to wear finer
garments than his king. Yet though Saint Louis used to
dress in plain gray wool without adornment, you come to
court in silk."

Silence fell as little groups turned to listen. Even Count
Louis, youngest brother of the King, looked up from the
dice-box which he was preparing to throw. Sir John of
Joinville rose from his stool with the aid of a staff which lay
beside him, while he fixed angry eyes on Enguerrand.

"Sir knight, when I was your age at the court of Saint
Louis, I had a brave green gown, fur-trimmed and very
costly. Master Robert de Sorbon, who was but a commoner

for all his wit and learning, took it on himself to reprove me
for overdressing. I told Master Robert, Sir, that my parents
had bequeathed me the proper rank to wear rich clothes
and that by so doing, I honored them. But he by wearing
good cloth dishonored his, who were clad in fustian.'"

Count Louis gave a shout of laughter, in which many
joined, for Sir Enguerrand's parents, though of decent birth,
were small provincial nobles who had never aspired to the
silks their son was wearing. But though Sir Enguerrand
scowled, he stood his ground. "What said Saint Louis?"

"He took the part of Master Robert, which made me angry because I thought I had spoken well. But a little while
later he sat himself down on the steps to his oratory and said
to his son, our good King's father, 'Sit down here close beside
me.' To young King Thibaut of Navarre, who was also present, he said, 'Sit by me, too.'

"The young men begged to excuse themselves, for they
thought it disrespectful to sit down touching the King. So
he ordered me to sit close up against him; and I did so while
the young men crouched on the lower step.

"The King bent forward his head until the four of us were
very close together, saying softly, 'I have a confession to
make. I took the part of Master Robert because I saw he was
embarrassed, but you must not take any notice of what I
said. Sir John of Joinville is right: you should dress as be-
comes your position, so that older men will never say you
have spent too much, nor younger men declare that you
have spent too little.'"

"This old man's memory," said Sir Enguerrand spitefully,

"is like the cruse of oil that fed Elisha. Every time he is in need, there is something in it."

"Sir John was a faithful servant," protested Count Louis, getting up to stroll over with the dice-box still in his hand.

"With your permission, Sir," cried Hugues de Bonville, "why was it that when our saintly King took the Cross a second time, this faithful servant who had loved him for so long refused to follow? As Saint Louis lay dying, I wonder what he thought of Sir John, who had turned his back on him in the hour of his greatest need."

Dead silence followed this remark as tears came welling into the eyes of the old man and trickled down his cheek. So stricken was he that though his lips moved, no sound came forth. In pity Count Louis hastened to say, "Sir John's record in King Louis's first Crusade is known to all. He needs make no defense for not going again."

The old man dashed away his tears with the back of his hand and made his little, old-fashioned bow towards Count Louis. "I thank you for your courtesy, fair lord; yet with your permission I will answer, for the question of Sir Hugues touches my honor."

"Then we will sit around your stool like the page boys," cried the Count, flinging himself to the ground to set an example. "I will not have it said that your honor is in question, but rather that you will teach us about Saint Louis."

Since neither Sir Enguerrand nor Sir Hugues dared contradict the King's brother, they sat themselves on the floor, only showing their disapproval by lolling back against the wall with eyes half-closed as they listened.

"When King Louis set out on his first Crusade, my lords," began the old man, "he was thirty-four, and I was ten years younger. My grandfather was with King Richard's Crusade which saved the coastal cities and had some slight success until it was destroyed by quarreling between the kings and the great lords who took part. Thereafter the cry arose that lesser nobles who had no selfish political ends would do God's work better. With such a Crusade went my two uncles in high hopes, but all its accomplishment was the taking of Constantinople and the opening of easy conquests in the fallen Empire which diverted men's energies from Palestine. Next John of Brienne, known to many as a good and valiant knight, was chosen King of Jerusalem and commander of a new Crusade which was directed against Egypt, because none can control the Holy Land without defeating the Moslem in the place where his strength lies. As my father often told me, this Crusade was nearly successful; but it bogged down at last in the gray mud of the Nile.

"After all these had failed, the Emperor Frederick went, with whom God forbid any Joinville should serve. The Holy Father had branded him as little better than an infidel, proclaiming a Crusade against him in Europe with all the indulgences of sin which are usually granted. Now whether the Devil aided him out of malice, or God to reproach us for our sins, the Emperor Frederick won Jerusalem by a treaty, so that for ten years the Holy City was Christian. At the end of that time, the infidel stretched out his hand and took it again. Thereafter our sainted King, Louis the Ninth, took the Cross to recover it once more.

"Judge then how eager I was to follow, being young and ready for adventure, besides having been brought up on the tales of Crusades in which my ancestors had given valiant service. My estate at that time was worth no more than a thousand livres; but I mortgaged all I could and hired eleven knights, besides their attendants, going shares in a ship with my cousin of Apremont to transport all of us to the Holy Land. I left on foot from my castle of Joinville, barefooted and with a pilgrim's staff in my hand, that I might fit myself for the business I was on by paying devotions to several places where there are holy relics. And often as my heart looked back to Joinville, to my wife and to my newborn son, I never turned my eyes in that direction, remembering that I was vowed to God for the present.

"Never was there any Crusade better prepared. Why, in Cyprus, where we assembled, the King had been buying for two years, so that huge piles of barrels were stacked up there like barns and grain lay in the great rounds, covered and protected by the sprouting of the outer layer like thatch. Nor was there room for wavering of purpose under our saintly master, who always thought of God first and his own people second, for there was never anything selfish about him.

"We sailed for Egypt, as all of you know, to win a victory over the infidel where he was strongest. All the sea as far as the eye could reach was covered with the canvas of our vessels, while our ships were bright with gilding and with pennons and coats-of-arms of the bravest knights in France. Never since that day have I seen such a glorious sight.

"God gave us victory at our landing, the King leaping up to his armpits into the surf to show the way. God brought us into the town of Damietta, whence the infidel had fled so fast that they had destroyed nothing. Now here it is certainly true that some of our people forgot our holy task in greed for plunder, yet no fault could be found in our King, who steadfastly set his face against such actions.

"Why was it, then, that after Damietta nothing more went right? We were cut off, half-starved, and plagued with scurvy, bogged down in the low-lying land of the Nile delta. Our King himself grew so weak with dysentery that they had to cut away his drawers and to lift him down from his horse and up again as was needed.

"We were surrounded, taken, massacred, or plundered to the skin. Even the King had nothing to wear but a sleeveless coat taken from a poor man. For my part, my captors spared me a wrap out of which we later made short tunics for myself and a little page whom I had with me.

"You all know how our King was threatened with torture and how, weak as he was, he could not be persuaded to make dishonorable terms or to pay ransom for himself alone, or for less than the whole army. Let me tell you, it took two days to weigh out fairly the one-half of the ransom, which we had to pay in advance. At the end, Philip of Nemours boasted in front of the King that we had cheated the Saracens out of ten thousand livres. Then the King would have had it all weighed over, so scrupulous of his word was he. But I trod hard on my lord Philip's foot and quickly answered that he had spoken in jest. The King, still uneasy charged the lord of Nemours to pay the whole sum upon his honor.

"In this way we departed from Egypt, the King with the bulk of the nobles who were left living after that disaster. But the sergeants and the simple knights and common people remained in captivity, awaiting full payment of the ransom.

"After we had arrived in Acre, the King took counsel of his lords about what he ought to do. The Queen Mother had written to tell him that there was trouble with England, so that he should return to France with speed. Nor after his defeat was he strong enough to conquer, so that the best that he could do would be defensive. The King's brothers and all the other nobles gave their votes for going home, saying it was useless to try and effect anything where they were. I alone begged the King to remain. I said he could be of use to the remnant of God's kingdom, while those kept prisoner would never be released except to him. Already the Moslem had failed to keep to his part of the treaty.

"For this advice I got black looks and words of abuse, so that afterwards I would not stand with the others, but went over to an embrasure, passing my arms through the bars of the window, my back turned to the rest. While I stood so, a man came up and leaned against me, putting his hands upon my head.

" 'Stop bothering me, Philip!' I said, for I thought it was Philip of Nemours. But as I jerked away impatiently, one of his hands came down in front of my face, and I saw the King's ring upon it.

"Then I stood very still, and the King said, 'I want to ask you how a young man like yourself could dare advise me in opposition to the great and wise men of France?'

" 'Your Majesty,' I said, 'I could not tell you to do a bad thing.'

" 'You mean, you thought it wrong for me to leave?'

" 'So help me God, I did,' I answered him.

"Then the King replied, 'If I stay, will you also?'

"We stayed four years and left the holy kingdom in better defense and better heart than we found it. Yet even so, its barons begged the King not to fortify a castle they had once possessed, no more than five leagues inland. 'For we could never supply it,' said they, 'considering that we do not control so much as a yard of the country outside the protection of our walls and ships.'

"We left after full four years, having done our duty and having got back our prisoners from Egypt. With great joy I returned to my castle of Joinville, from which I had been so long away — and in sad case I found it. My poor people, taxed for the Crusade and taxed again for the ransom, hounded by the officers of the King and in addition by those of the Count of Champagne, my overlord, had never anyone to take their part. Nor was the rest of the kingdom in better case, so that the administration of the realm came perilously near to breaking down.

"All this the King perceived as well as I, and we all know how he devoted himself for many years to his people's welfare. He never spoke much of the Crusade, but it was at that time that he ceased to wear scarlet cloth or furred garments

such as were proper to his rank. I think he never forgot a
tale which was reported by one who went to Damascus buying horn and glue for our bows. He had come across an old
man in the bazaar who had called out mockingly, 'Once
long ago I saw King Baldwin of Jerusalem, who was a leper,
defeating Saladin, though Baldwin had only three hundred
men at his back against Saladin's three thousand. But now
you are brought so low that we take you in the fields, just as
if you were cattle.' No doubt the saintly King held himself
unworthy of being the champion of God, and he blamed his
faults for having caused the destruction of so many.

"For my part, I learned to doubt whether God would ever
bless a Christian Crusade, seeing that the greatest King and
the most saintly man alive had no better fortune. Besides,
seeing how much we had been needed in France while we
were away, I thought God wished me to devote the rest of
my life to my estate of Joinville, where He had set me to rule
in the first place.

"When the King took the Cross again, my lords, he was
already over fifty and in such poor health that he let me
carry him in my arms rather than walk. Who advised him
I do not know, any more than I can discover who advised
many Popes to proclaim Crusades against Christian emperors or countries or cities with whom they happened to
quarrel. Our saintly King was not always right, my lords,
as I would tell him when he asked my advice. I told him so
at this time, and it is true that he was displeased.

"He set out, and he did not return. Half the nobility of

France died with him on that Crusade, mostly of plague. In sum, we lost the best King in the world and accomplished nothing. My heart was sore when I heard of his death because we had parted with a difference of opinion between us. Seeing, however, that the good King was already in Heaven, I trusted that he had learned to understand me.

"Last year, when the Pope declared him a Saint, which was in my opinion no more than something long due, I prayed to him in my chapel at Joinville, as I had long wished the Church would permit me to pray. That very night by God's grace I dreamed I saw the King standing in front of my chapel, clad in his sober gray with a black surcoat and a cotton cap upon his head. He was marvelously glad to see me, and I him.

" 'My lord,' I said, for speech in dreams is often foolish, 'when you go away from Joinville, I will make a place for you in a house I own in a village called Chevillon.'

" 'My lord of Joinville,' answered the King, laughing at me, 'I have no wish to go away so soon.'

"At this I woke with a heart at peace over the soreness of our last parting on earth. Since he had desired to stay in Joinville, I built him an altar to the glory of God in my chapel, endowing masses in his memory. If Saint Louis has forgiven me, then, is there any man who has a right to reflect upon my honor?"

"I do not think there is," agreed Count Louis gravely. A thought seemed to strike him, and he turned to Sir Hugues of Bonville. "Tell me, Lord Chamberlain, if King Philip were to take the Cross, as he has talked of doing, would you follow him overseas, or would you not?"

"To doubt that I would is to doubt my honor," cried the Chamberlain.

Count Louis smiled. "You would follow your liege lord, but would you do so from loyalty to him or love of God? Would you go to the East in King Philip's train or because you believe it was a holy war?"

The lord of Bonville hesitated, but Enguerrand of Montigny had a quicker wit.

"I should follow my lord the King," said he, looking around him with the air of one who is going to say something clever. "But of those who advised him to take the Cross, I should first ask some questions." He leaned back against the wall, drawling out his words while he watched their effect. " 'My lords bishops, eloquent preachers, or whosoever you be, have you counted how often Popes have cried holy war for unholy reasons and thrown Christendom into turmoil to gain their own ends? Have you seen the agents of Holy Church selling redemption from crusader vows on the street corners, in the very shadow of Saint Peter's, to raise money? Have you noticed how while the Church cries poor, her bishops ride like princes and her fat abbots gorge themselves like pigs? Have you reckoned how little God cared about His kingdom, which even Saint Louis could not save in the end? For seven years now those who were once the barons of the Holy Land have toiled as slaves in Egypt or starved as refugees in the kingdom of Cyprus. The great city of Acre, which was their capital, is a heap of ruins, sheltering a few wretched peasants in its broken cellars. In God's name, then, my lords bishops or preachers, inform me for what reason you still maintain there is such a thing as a holy war?' "

EPILOGUE

The Last Crusader

1464

THE IMPULSE towards a great Crusade had died with Saint Louis. King Philip the Fair talked of an expedition, but only because he needed a pretext for taxing the Church. Rulers were too busy with rivalries in Europe. Popes had grown weak, and clever men were disillusioned. Faith still died hard, however. Many liked to look back to the ideal of Pope Urban of a Christendom at peace with itself an enlisted under the banner of God. Conferences discussed Crusades, and lords made promises which dwindled away in the face of reality.

The infidel, secure in his domains, grew steadily stronger. In a century the Turks had swept through Asia Minor and were knocking at the gates of Constantinople, once the Queen of Cities. Here the Greek Emperors had regained their throne after fifty years of Latin conquest. Constantinople was still the most civilized city in the world, sheltering the arts and learning of the Roman Empire, which had been enshrined in her for a thousand years. Yet for all its visible glory, Constantinople was dying, its population shrunk, its empire shattered by Doge Dandolo and never reconquered. The lasting achievement of the great Crusades had proved to be the destruction of an empire which had been the bulwark of Christendon.

The Queen of Cities fell, and Saint Sophia, after a thousand years as a Christian church, became a mosque. The lamp of learning went out as the invaders swept past the city into Europe.

It was at this time that the last crusader set out to the rescue. He was a strange man for the purpose, this Pope Pius, who had been Aeneus Sylvius, an author of very worldly books, an intriguing politician, and a churchman only in middle life — and out of ambition. It was never entirely clear whether his determination to rescue Constantinople arose from the worldling's love of classical learning, from the statesman's fear of the conquest of Europe, or from the Holy Father's concern for religion. Perhaps for all these reasons, Pius II took the Cross himself to shame the rulers of Europe into following his lead.

He set out from Saint Peter's to go to Ancona, a port of his own in which he had caused to be assembled a fleet of transports at his own expense. He traveled slowly, though in somewhat martial style, with mounted troopers ahead and foot soldiers trailing behind. In the middle came his baggage mules and his personal attendants, mostly clerical and riding at the Pope's expense on well-fed ponies. Though he was not yet sixty, Pius's strength was failing, and the journey had prostrated him alarmingly. Since he would go on, they laid him in a litter as they wound through the dusty roads towards Ancona.

About fifteen miles outside the port the doctor, who was riding constantly beside the litter, made a signal with his hand, whereat the cavalcade stumbled to a halt. He got off his mule to mix a cordial out of wine and water proffered by an attendant, to which he added a drop or two out of a little bottle he wore around his neck. One of the men who walked beside the litter to fan the sick man and brush away the flies stooped over to raise the Pope in his arms so that he could drink. Some of the liquid dribbled out of the corners of the sick man's mouth, and they wiped him with a napkin. They bathed his face and hands, readjusting the curtains to keep out of the sun.

"Holy Father," said the doctor, laying the sick man's hand down gently, "will it please you to rest during the heat of the day . . . there is an inn."

The sick man's breathing was harsh and noisy. The doctor bent down with an ear toward the pallid lips. ". . . too long on the road," murmured the dying Pope. "The King of Hungary . . . the Emperor . . . the King of France . . .

I can shame them into coming, but how long will they wait?
. . . How far to Ancona?"

"Some fifteen miles," the doctor said.

"Go on! Go on! We must be there by nightfall."

The doctor got back on his horse again, shaking his head.

"The captain asked at the inn whether the armies were
embarking, but the landlord did not know what armies he
meant," remarked the Pope's personal secretary, riding beside the doctor.

"Strange, since the armies are no more than fifteen miles
away," remarked the doctor.

"Very strange."

"One would imagine they'd scour the countryside for supplies."

"Indeed one would."

"Hm!" grunted the doctor, cutting off conversation as he
turned to watch his patient.

"Will he last till Ancona?" murmured the secretary.

The doctor shrugged. "If God wills it."

Ancona lay in a valley between two hills debouching from
a ridge of land along which the road traveled. After some
hours they came in sight of it; and the secretary, shading his
eyes from the westering sun, looked down on the trim little
harbor crowded with shipping and the blue Adriatic beyond. The troopers riding ahead of him cut off his vision of
the town creeping up the slopes, with vineyards and cypress
trees outside its wall.

The captain of the troopers fell back beside him and bent
over to murmur confidentially in his ear, "No tents!"

"Eh, what?"

"No army tents outside the city. None at all."

The secretary craned his neck to peer over the troopers; but being a small round man on a small round pony, he could not do so. "Better stop again," he said to the doctor, "before we go down to Ancona."

The doctor called a halt: and while he ministered to his patient, the secretary rode up to the front of the column. Ancona, glistening in the sun, was a jumble of gray walls and tiled roofs. The slopes were empty of encampments, but there was a crowd of people on the road which mounted the hill beside the streamlet bringing water into the town.

"They must have embarked," said the secretary puzzled. "Embarked already and are sending home their carriers."

"I daresay," said the captain in unconvincing tones.

The secretary gave a nervous laugh. "You know," he explained to the captain, "I never was yet with an army, and it surprises me to see so many people left behind."

"Hm, yes," said the captain, watching the people stream out of the gates of the town. "Beggars, pedlars, mountebanks, washerwomen . . . there is always riffraff following an army."

"How far to Ancona?" mumbled the sick man as the secretary returned.

The secretary bent over him. "Five miles only. The town is in plain sight."

"Lift me up, then. Prop me on pillows!" He struggled to rise. "I am getting better . . . only weak. Did you make out the escutcheons?"

"Escutcheons?" For a moment the secretary was puzzled. "Oh, the banners of the army! It is not to be seen, for they have just embarked. The beggars and pedlars and mule trains are going home."

The Pope smiled. "The King of France . . . the King of Hungary . . . the King of Spain . . . I shamed them into it. We are late at the rendezvous because of this weakness of mine. Push on!"

The train lumbered forward. There were men leading the horses of the litter while others held poles attached to it to steady it from undue movement. They went down a dip in the ridge, losing sight of Ancona and of the straggling crowds trailing up the road towards them.

When these came into view again, they were much nearer. The secretary dug his spurs into his palfrey and bumped up the road to ride by the captain, who pointed at the nearest group not half a mile distant. "That's not cripples and women and riffraff. Those are men!"

"Muleteers perhaps," guessed the secretary wildly. "They must have loaded a great deal of baggage."

The captain looked contemptuous. "Where are the mules?" With a sudden impulse he urged his horse into a trot. The secretary raced after him on his short-legged pony, who had never in his comfortable life been spurred so hard.

The men coming up the road were a hard-bitten lot, lugging packs of various sizes and wearing, for the most part, long knives in their belts. "Whither away?" shouted the captain to the foremost.

He took no notice and plodded by, a black-bearded ruffian with an ugly scowl for the two mounted men. "What's that to you?" called someone from a group which followed at his heels.

The secretary reined up panting. "The Holy Father — " Deliberately one of the men halted in front of him and spat. The gesture was so unmistakable that the secretary's mouth hung literally open. The crudity affected him like outright blasphemy, and he had no answer for it. The captain, used though he was to roughness, flushed indignantly and half drew out his sword. Seeing, however, that more men were hurrying up the road and knives were flashing in several people's hands, he slammed it back and, rising in his stirrups, beckoned to the troopers a few hundred yards behind him.

"Now see here, men," he said bluntly, ". . . sailors, aren't you? . . . what's the trouble?"

A confusion of curses and angry cries arose from the men, who by this time numbered some fifty or more, while others appearing around a bend in the road hastened forward to see what was going on.

"You there!" yelled the captain, drawing his sword with a sudden movement to point at a grizzled giant with a nose smashed crooked and a cauliflower ear who was standing in the front. "Speak out! What's the matter?"

"Matter? God blast you for a fool! No voyage, no pay. That's the matter! And I from Genoa! By the time that I get back there, season's half over, and I can starve on the beach. The Holy Father," he mimicked the secretary's tone. "He can afford his follies. He isn't a poor man!"

"But I don't understand," shrieked the secretary over the
sound of the clamor which the eloquence of the big man had
aroused. "Who are these people?"

"The sailors of the fleet," said the captain grimly. "They're
going home."

"B-but how shall we go overseas? The Kings? The Emperor?"

"I knew it," the captain said. "I knew it when there were
no tents. Oh, I knew it when that innkeeper had not heard
of an army. I — " He broke off, finding himself talking to
air. The secretary had wrenched his pony around and was
tearing back up the road, the skirts of his long gown flapping
with his movements.

The Pope had been raised a little on his cushions. "They
tell me that men are sent out to meet us. The Kings . . . the
Emperor?"

The secretary took a deep breath and let it out slowly,
trying to control his panting and speak calmly. "The Kings
will wait to receive you in Ancona. This is nothing but the
rabble of the town coming out to greet you. If it please you,
I will draw the curtains of your litter lest they imagine that
you are too weak to embark. In any case, it would be better
if you would go to sleep so that you may not find it too tiring
to receive the great ones."

He drew the curtains of the litter gently, but the doctor
leaned over to stay his hand. "Without the breeze, it will be
like an oven. How can he bear it?"

"He must bear it," said the secretary, speaking softly lest
the ears of the dying man catch what he was saying. "None

of the Kings or princes came — not one of those whom he thought to shame by coming himself. The fleet is breaking up, and all the sailors who were hired for the voyage are going home. Close the curtains lest he see them! It is better that he stifle while still thinking that the great ones are waiting to receive him in Ancona."

The doctor closed the curtains, fastening them lest they gape open with some sudden movement. Slowly, painfully, the litter lurched down the road.